LABORATORY

INSTRUMENTATION

IN PSYCHOLOGY

By
WILLIAM W. GRINGS
Associate Professor of Psychology
University of Southern California

THE NATIONAL PRESS
Palo Alto, California

Preface

The following manual represents a selection from the teaching materials which the writer has used for a number of years in a one-semester course on laboratory apparatus and technique. For a time, consideration was given to the expansion of the materials into a comprehensive treatment of the subject matter, and toward this end the writer has cooperated with Dr. George Mount of the University of California at Los Angeles. Meanwhile, an interest in the use of the materials already available has been expressed by colleagues with the result that the accompanying sections have been prepared in lithoprinted form. The general perspective of the undertaking has been outlined in Chapter 1 and will therefore not be repeated here.

The author is indebted to numerous students and colleagues who have contributed to this work. There are three persons in particular who should be mentioned: Dr. Harold Trueblood, who for four years worked with the writer in the laboratory and evaluated early drafts of these materials; Dr. George Mount, who for two years collaborated with the writer on a related undertaking and reviewed Chapters 2, 3, and 5; and Dr. John Stamm, who for two years used these instructional materials, made numerous contributions to their laboratory applications, and reviewed Chapters 2 and 8.

Grateful acknowledgment is also made to the many individuals, publishers, and manufacturers who have contributed illustration material. The list is too long to give here but acknowledgment is indicated with each illustration. Because these materials were incorporated in teaching and lecture notes for a long time before being set down in a reference form, it is probable that the source of some idea or manner of illustrating a problem may have been lost or overlooked. It is hoped that such failures of acknowledgment are not numerous.

W. W. G.

Los Angeles, California
September 1, 1954

Contents

CHAPTER 1

Introduction

THE PSYCHOLOGY LABORATORY

Historically, psychology was introduced to its laboratory largely through biology and physics, and it was soon identified by its brass instruments. The "brass instrument era" was so strong that some psychologists were inclined to judge the value of a university research potential in terms of the number and quality of the instruments it possessed, and to a certain degree by the amount of shine. The reaction against this emphasis upon apparatus has been strong. One still hears occasionally that psychology has outgrown its brass instruments, although about equally often the comment is made that psychologists have traded their brass instruments for electronic instruments.

Whatever the relative emphasis on matters pertaining to instrumentation in psychology, the important fact remains that there are many significant problems in psychology which can be studied best under controlled laboratory conditions. This suggests such goals as controlling the external environment of the organism(s) whose behavior is being observed, regulating or manipulating physical stimuli present, and providing instrumental aids for observing, measuring, or recording the behavior. These are the situations which are basic to the use of the term "laboratory psychology" in this context. Laboratory psychology from the standpoint of its psychological subject matter is not restrictive. Therefore, its study is not so much a study of the "psychology" it contains as it is the kinds of laboratory situations which have found use.

Because the material which follows represents only a small portion of the subject matter, it must remain only representative of the laboratory in psychology. The categories chosen are used for convenience only, although some correspond roughly to areas in which research interests concentrate.

THE ROLE OF INSTRUMENTATION

The most significant functions of laboratory instruments are measurement and control. Since the scientist's principal activities are observations under controlled conditions, one index of the usefulness of instruments to experimenting psychologists is the extent to which they facilitate the observation, quantification, and control of variables relevant to the psychological situation.

When the behavior being observed involves changes in physical energy (mechanical, electrical, etc.), specialized instruments may be much better able to observe than the unaided human sense. This makes possible not only the extension of the range of the senses but also a reduction in the "personal equation" of observation. Besides minimizing reliance on human watchfulness, instruments can be useful labor savers, reducing the drudgery of meticulous observation.

For conditions that are varying, instruments are able to register changes in quantity, and if it is so desired they can serve in a closed loop, self-regulatory system maintaining stable conditions. Many psychological laboratory instruments are control servomechanisms. In the establishment of controlled experimental conditions, measurement of all relevant variables may be aided by instruments.

A likely misinterpretation of the role of instruments in psychology may arise from the fact that all instruments are physical in nature, and they measure physical variables. It might be argued that the use of instruments makes the researcher too limited to the correlation of physical and psychological variables, or to the definition of behavior variables in terms of those of physics. This point of view overlooks some of the most significant roles of instruments as recorders—for example, magnetic recordings of verbal behavior or photographic records of group behavior. The simplest control functions, such as those of timing an interval or reducing distracting stimuli, are present in nearly every observational situation.

The applications of instruments discussed here will range widely. The study of sensory phenomena requires measurement and control of the particular energies to which the sense organ is sensitive. Brain-wave investigation requires instruments for picking up minute electrical potentials, amplifying them, and registering or recording them without distortion. Learning studies typically control time and exposure characteristics of the stimulus situation and register responses, as do apparatus tests of individual differences. Measures of psychological stress rely to a large degree on instruments for measuring physiological reaction.

THE NEED FOR STUDY OF INSTRUMENTATION

It is not sufficient to become aware only of the uses of instruments in laboratory study, for the limitations to such use loom equally large. The more complicated the instrument becomes, the more subject it is to errors of various sorts; and the more complex it is, the more likely it is to be used incorrectly in a situation for which it was probably not designed.

On the one hand, without a certain degree of intimate familiarity with instruments the laboratory worker may be unaware of powerful technical aids to his research. As a result, his measurements may be more crude than necessary, or his control of physical factors more gross. Whereas, at the other extreme, lack of acquaintance with instrumentation may lead to exaggerated expectations from instrumental aids or a failure to control instrument error appropriately.

The problems associated with the evaluation of instruments will be considered later in connection with specific apparatus. Important topics are accuracy, sensitivity, range, backlash or backward action, distortion, signal to noise ratio, reliability.

SCOPE OF THE BOOK

In a subject matter as diversified as the present-day psychology laboratory, certain limitations need to be placed on the scope of the discussion. An indication will be given of major omissions from the general subject matter, and a definition will be made of the level at which the treatment will progress.

There are several major areas of information which were left out intentionally. The most significant of these is the animal laboratory, for the literature on the laboratory use of animals is extensive. The omission was made for numerous reasons: (a) There was a need to keep this discussion brief. (b) Most of what is said in other contexts (such as recording and timing) applies equally well to animal work. (c) Excellent sources of this information are available through the works of Farris (1), Farris and Griffith (2), Munn (3), and others.

Another area omitted is the application of apparatus to the measurement of individual differences in capacity to perform certain tasks. This is the subject of apparatus tests; again much of what is discussed applies to this topic, and other source material is available (4). A subject matter of increasing importance to psychology which is left out deals with calculating and computing devices. This area is so extensive that it could hardly be treated in this context.

From the standpoint of the student, the most noticeable omission is a discussion of information and problems associated with the design and construction of one's own laboratory equipment. Because it will probably always be necessary to construct apparatus to fit specific research needs, the machine and electrical shops occupy positions of central importance in a psychological laboratory. There are numerous excellent references on shop practice and a few, such as 5, 6, 7, 10, 11, 12, and 13, which give particular attention to apparatus problems. Still another area omitted is laboratory photography, again because of excellent source material readily available.

It had originally been planned to include the extensive

bibliography which was compiled in connection with this discussion, but it is so long (over 1000 entries) that this has become impractical. If, however, any interested reader desires a mimeographed copy of the bibliography, it may be obtained at cost from the author. (Also, see Andrews, 9.)

The level at which the following discussion proceeds can be indicated in terms of the persons for whom it is primarily intended and the general background or prerequisites which it assumes. The material is intended to be an introduction to the laboratory directed at graduate students or professional people who desire enough detail to get started into an area of research. Where space permits, references to more advanced sources are cited to provide a basis for following through to a higher level. Information will seldom be complete at the level of the research specialist, although occasionally he may find new material or circuits.

There are two essential prerequisites to the maximum use of the book. One is a general acquaintance with the subject matter of elementary physics. The other is at least some exposure to the basic principles of electronics (8). In teaching this material, the author has found it necessary to devote several weeks of preliminary discussion to the subjects of elementary electricity, electronics, and mechanics.

SOURCES OF APPARATUS

The presentation of a complete list of manufacturers of instruments to be considered throughout this book would be of prohibitive length. The most complete source of such information known to the author is termed the *Instrument index* and is published as an extra issue of the periodical *Instruments* by the Instruments Publishing Co., 921 Ridge Ave., Pittsburgh 12, Pa. This presents (1) an index to instruments and apparatus; (2) a list of laboratory supply houses; and (3) a directory of manufacturers. Other periodicals of applied physics, such as the *Review of scientific instruments,* published by the American Institute of Physics, 57 East 55th St., New York 22, N. Y., and *Electronics,* published by the McGraw-Hill Book Co., present this type of procurement information periodically. In addition, all of the above give brief descriptions of new apparatus.

A few years ago a committee of the American Psychological Association was appointed to collect and report information on the matter of sources of psychology laboratory equipment. A source list was compiled and distributed by the APA central office. It contains most of the major suppliers.

Changes are so frequent in commercial models of instruments that it is essential that every laboratory maintain some form of file of manufacturers' literature. This file provides an excellent source of information for the student, for many manufacturers publish trade notes which contain much technical information of value. An example of this type of literature is the *Oscillographer,* a quarterly on cathode-ray oscillography, published by the Allen B. DuMont Laboratories, Clifton, N. J. Another is *Scientific apparatus and methods,* also a quarterly, published by E. H. Sargent & Co., Chicago, Ill.

Psychological periodicals remain the main source of up-to-date information about the application of instruments in psychology. Particularly noteworthy at the present time is the apparatus section of the *American journal of psychology.* Similar discussions occur frequently in the *Journal of experimental psychology,* the *Journal of general psychology,* and the *Journal of psychology.*

REFERENCES

1. FARRIS, E. J. (Ed.) *The care and breeding of laboratory animals.* New York: John Wiley & Sons, Inc., 1950.
2. FARRIS, E. J., and GRIFFITH, J. Q. *The rat in laboratory investigation.* Philadelphia: J. B. Lippincott Co., 1949.
3. MUNN, N. L. *Handbook of psychological research on the rat.* New York: Houghton Mifflin Co., 1950.

4. MELTON, A. W. (Ed.) *Apparatus tests.* Washington, D. C.: U. S. Government Printing Office, 1947. (AAF Aviation Psychol. Prog. Research Report No. 4.)
5. GLASSER, O. *Medical physics.* Chicago: Yearbook Publishing Co., Vol. 1, 1944, Vol. 2, 1950.
6. STRONG, J. *Procedures in experimental physics.* New York: Prentice-Hall, Inc., 1946.
7. DICKINSON, C. J. *Electrophysiological technique.* London: Electronic Engineering, 1950.
8. AARONSON, M. H. *Electronic circuitry for instruments and equipment.* Pittsburgh: Instruments Publishing Co., 1953.
9. ANDREWS, T. G. Some psychological apparatus: a classified bibliography, *Psychol. monogr.*, 1948, No. 289, Vol. 62, No. 2.
10. COOPER, H. J. *Scientific instruments.* New York: Chemical Publishing Co., Inc., I, 1946; II, 1949.
11. REILLY, J., and RAE, W. N. *Physico-chemical methods.* New York: D. Von Nostrand Co., Inc., 1939, 2 Vols.
12. WHITEHEAD, T. N. *The design and use of instruments and accurate mechanisms.* New York: Macmillan, 1934.
13. WILSON, E. B. *An introduction to scientific research.* New York: McGraw-Hill Book Co., Inc., 1952. (Chapter 5. The design of apparatus.)

CHAPTER 2

Behavior Recording Systems

Underlying every laboratory investigation in psychology is some form of response recording. At one extreme of record keeping the subject, experimenter, or other observer makes entries upon a record sheet. At the other extreme, instruments automatically record in permanent form an accurate account of all relevant data. Between these points lie various degrees of application of instrumental recording devices with the common aim of providing as true a record as possible of phenomena under observation. It is the purpose of this section to review some of the most frequently used laboratory recording systems utilizing apparatus and to consider the essential requirements of such devices. The typical recording system consists of a device for picking up the material to be recorded, a device for transmitting it to the registration device (in amplified form, if necessary), a registration device for putting it on a recording surface, and a chart drive for presenting the recording surface (1).

KYMOGRAPHS AND POLYGRAPHS

The most familiar laboratory recorder is the *kymograph*, or revolving drum, equipped with a recording surface on which the movements of styli, magnetic markers, or pneumatic registration devices are inscribed (Fig. 2-1). When two or more such drums are used in combination to permit completion of longer records, the apparatus is termed a long-paper kymograph. The number of factors which may be recorded and the length of record is limited only by the space requirements of the system recorded and the dimensions of the recording surface.

The typical *polygraph* differs from the kymograph in that the recording surface is driven across a rack on which the registration devices are mounted (Fig. 2 - 2).

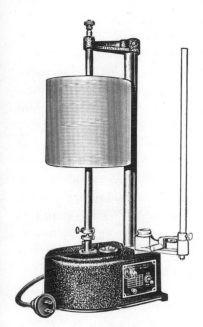

Fig. 2 - 1—An electrically driven kymograph. (Courtesy Phipps & Bird, Inc., Richmond, Va.)

Fig. 2 - 2—A horizontal polygraph. (Courtesy Phipps & Bird, Inc., Richmond, Va.)

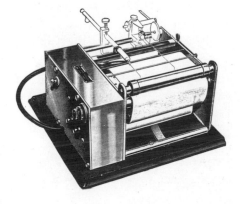
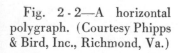

DIRECT RECORDING SURFACES AND TECHNIQUES

The recording surfaces used with these devices take several forms. *Smoked-paper* surfaces have been common with kymographs. Such a surface has the advantage that distinctive markings may be made with a very small amount of friction between the surface and registration device. It has the disadvantage that it cannot be utilized in long rolls and must be fixed with a material such as shellac for preservation. Smoking of the surface is accomplished by passing kymograph paper, glazed surface out, through a smoky flame. This is generally done with the paper on the recording drum in order that the metal may carry away the heat and prevent scorching of the paper. Only a very thin uniform layer of carbon is required, for a thick deposit increases friction and clogs the registration device.

The smoke may be secured from any source which yields a fine-grained, dry deposit. The flame of illuminating gas from a Bunsen burner with a specially prepared fishtail outlet is frequently preferred. Other sources include burning turpentine, camphor, kerosene, or paraffin. When a smoked record has been completed, it is made permanent by passing it through a fixative solution and permitting it to dry. A common fixative solution consists of commercial shellac diluted with ten parts of ethanol with a small amount of glycerine added to prevent brittleness. Other recommended solutions include resin dissolved in ethanol, or plastic (2). Such solutions may be used again with occasional filtering and care to prevent evaporation.

Pen-and-ink recording is commonly employed in commercial polygraphs. Surfaces range from adding machine tape to specially calibrated self-folding sheets or rolls. Each has advantages in certain situations. In many cases the glossy surface of the typical kymograph paper, mentioned above for smoked recording, may be used to advantage with ink. The pens with which the records are made also vary widely. In some cases, the pen may consist of an ink reservoir somewhat similar to a familiar pen with the ink being fed through a reedlike slit in contact with the surface. An example of such a recorder is the Cambridge chronograph.

Another common ink device is the capillary pen. This instrument, when attached to a tambour or signal magnet, resembles the conventional stylus in appearance (Fig. 2 - 3). The stylus portion consists of a fine hollow metal tube, one end of which is held in light contact with the paper by a gravity or

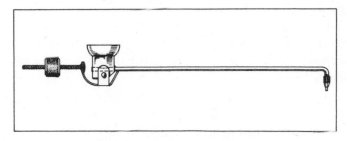

Fig. 2 - 3—A capillary pen. (Courtesy Associated Research, Inc., Chicago)

spring arrangement. The other end dips in a stationary ink reservoir from which the ink flows by capillary action through the pen to the surface. For many uses a simple capillary pen may be constructed by drawing a piece of fine glass tubing out to a capillary point and attaching it to the reed of a conventional stylus (3).

Specially prepared ink is required for maximum results with capillary pens. Most pen manufacturers supply inks designed for, or recommended for use with, their pens. A formula for such an ink (as recommended by Offner Electronics Inc. for use with their oscillographs) consists of glycerine 50 cc, ethanol 50 cc, eosin-Y 2.3 grams, phenol .1 gram, and water to make one liter.

Ink recording systems have the advantages of immediate availability of the record, the possibility of lengthy records, and general ease of use. There are, however, an equal number of disadvantages which must be evaluated in terms of the requirements of a particular recording situation. Most pens have considerable mass which may affect the sensitivity of the recorder and produce lag and overshooting. A certain amount of friction between the pen point and recording surface is necessary in order for the ink to flow. In general, ink recording systems have been satisfactorily used with signal magnets, pressure recording devices, electric current measuring devices, and oscillographic recordings such as those involved in electroencephalography.

Another recording surface which is applicable to both kymographs and polygraphs consists of a light-weight paper, one side of which is coated with a thin layer of wax. The required tracing is made by scratching or melting of this wax with a stylus comparable to that employed with smoked surfaces (4). When considerable power is available to operate the styli such *waxed papers* have the advantage that they may be handled conveniently in long rolls, require no fixatives, and are immediately available for use (Fig. 2 - 4). Their chief disadvantage arises from the fact that considerable pressure of the stylus on the surface is required for a satisfactory tracing; which in turn increases the friction in the system, thereby reducing sensitivity and increasing distortion. Some commercial recorders employing this type of surface reduce this disadvantage materially by employing a hot wire stylus. The wax is melted at the point of contact, and the resulting friction between stylus and surface is much reduced. For a description of such heating devices note Wendt (1).

In recording situations where the chief concern is for counting the number of times something occurs, or in designating the onset and cessation of specific events, a system of *spark recording* may be used to advantage. It is adaptable to a kymograph or polygraph. The record is made by causing a spark to jump from the point of a stylus through a recording paper to a metallic base plate such as a metal kymograph drum. As the spark passes through the paper, it burns a hole, melts wax, or removes carbon, depending on whether the recording surface is plain, waxed, or smoked. In such a situation, the stylus need not be in direct contact with the surface, thereby eliminating stylus-surface friction.

The spark is often produced by introducing the stylus and base plate into the secondary of an inductorium. If a continuous record of the movements of the stylus is desired (as when

Fig. 2 - 4—A chronograph employing a wax-paper surface. (Courtesy Gaertner Scientific Corp., Chicago, Ill.)

recording from a tambour) the sparks may be spaced at uniform intervals by the introduction of a timing device into the inductorium circuit. The course of the stylus is thus recorded as a line of holes. Such a procedure, however, introduces the possibility of error due to the fact that the course of the spark may not always be in a direct path from the stylus to the drum. Variations in the insulating properties of the paper, the conductivity of the kymograph drum surface, and changes in the stylus point, due to burning, may cause the spark to jump some-what to the side of its most direct course.

Other arrangements such as punch tapes, pencils, ball-point pens, and mechanical printers find less frequent applica-tion in psychological recordings. The requirements of a par-ticular situation in which a kymographic or polygraphic rec-ord is to be made will in each case determine the surface to be used, the most appropriate drive mechanism for that sur-face, and the most advantageous registration device.

PHOTOGRAPHIC RECORDING

Photographic recorders, or *photokymographs* as they are commonly called, employ a recording surface of light-sensi-tive film, plate, or paper on which are registered the move-ments of some form of light and shadow system which corre-sponds to the phenomenon under observation. The most com-mon surfaces are photosensitive films and papers, and the most common drive mechanisms are similar to those of a polygraph —consisting of a supply roller, a drive roller, and a regis-tration plate or "screen" of some sort. The appropriate regis-tration on the recording surface is accomplished through (a) control of a recording light beam by mirrors or other light re-flecting means, (b) shadow producing devices, (c) focused images, (d) intermittent light sources, and (e) intensity changes in light incident upon the surface.

Several procedures are used for controlling the exposure of the sensitive surface to light. The simplest recorder employs no lenses and has a small slit by which the surface passes. A uniform, diffuse light (wash light) shines on the slit, such that the shadow of a reed across the slit will result in an unexposed trace on an otherwise exposed surface. Or, the entire area may be dark except for a concentrated line of light which is directed onto the slit. The line is most frequently produced by the image of a straight filament bulb which is directed by a mirror and lens system into the slit. This record appears as a trace of exposed (dark) area on an otherwise unexposed surface.

A simple slit is inappropriate for use with high speeds of recording, since the light entering the slit is not concentrated. To overcome this limitation, a cylindrical lens is often used to concentrate the light falling on the slit, converging it to a focus on the sensitive surface. With such an arrangement, greater paper speeds may be obtained.

When shadow recording is used, and the record is produced by passing a stylus in front of a uniformly illuminated slit, a time scale can be obtained by periodically interrupting the wash light. Each one of these interruptions gives a narrow strip of unexposed surface. To show amplitude of response, a grid of fine wires may be introduced in the slit such that fine lines of unexposed surface occur at equal distances throughout the width of the slit. By having some grid wires thicker than others, certain of the grid lines can be accentuated.

A typical slit-type photokymograph for recording the response of a d'Arsonval galvanometer is shown in Figure 2-5. The light from a straight filament bulb is reflected from a mir-

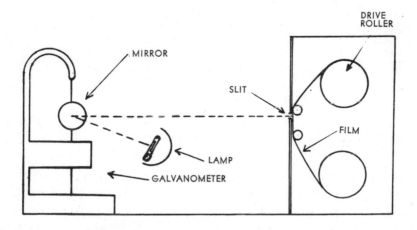

Fig. 2-5—A slit photokymograph for recording the response of a d'Arsonval galvanometer

ror, which is attached to the coil of a galvanometer, and passes through the slit to the sensitive paper or film. As the galvanometer responds to changes in the external system with which it is connected, the mirror turns. This alters the angle between the light source and the mirror, and causes the light to move along the slit. A time scale can be added by introducing an intermittent light which produces a dot or line on the surface each time it is on.

Many photographic recorders are modifications of the ordinary camera and focus an image of the actual object being observed onto the sensitive surface. They are typically equipped with a moving film or paper in the same way as the slit type photorecorders. Two common examples of such photographic recorders are the cameras for taking pictures of the screen of cathode-ray oscillographs, and commercial ophthalmograph cameras for recording eye movements.

REGISTRATION DEVICES

MECHANICALLY OPERATED STYLI

The most common registration device is the mechanically operated lever. It consists of a stylus operating about a fulcrum and powered by an applied force. In the forms most commonly used for recording purposes the fulcrum may be located either at the end with the point of application of force between it and the writing point or between the point of application of force and the writing point. Because of the mechanical nature of such a lever, the influence of mass factors is very important. Amplification is possible by having the distance from the point of application of force to the fulcrum be less than the distance of the writing point from the fulcrum. Such amplification, however, influences the inertia of the lever.

The effective mass of a lever depends in part on its moment of inertia, which is equal to one-third the product of the total weight in grams and the square of the total length in centimeters—assuming that the weight is uniformly distributed and the fulcrum is at one end. The effective mass of a stylus lever is dependent also upon degree of magnification, being much greater at high magnification than at low magnification. It may be computed by dividing the moment of inertia by the square of the distance of the fulcrum from the point of application of force. For minimum effective mass a mechanical stylus lever should be as short as possible, as light as possible, and operating at as low a magnification ratio as is possible.

The forms which such mechanical levers take differ with the system being recorded. In its simplest form, the lever is a light stylus reed with a writing point which scratches the surface of a smoked drum, or which passes in front of the slit of a photorecorder. The applied force may come directly from the movement being observed; or there may be an intermediate lever system, electrical system, pneumatic system, or the like, between the observed phenomenon and the point of application of force. In more complicated forms, the stylus may consist of a fine metal capillary tube which carries ink from a reservoir to the recording surface. The lever, as such, forms a basic part of most of the registration devices mentioned later. Regardless of its modification, its basic function will depend upon length, weight, and magnification ratio.

Pressure Recorders

The class name for pressure recorders is *manometer*. The main types differ in respect to whether the pressure system is pneumatic (compressible) or liquid (incompressible). The most common air-pressure registration devices are *tambours*— modifications of which are also applicable to liquid systems. The typical tambour consists of a metal chamber with an intake tube and an open side (Fig. 2 - 6a). The open side is covered with a diaphragm of specially constructed rubber or metal. Being flexible, the diaphragm responds to changes in pressure introduced into the chamber through the input tube. Movements of the diaphragm are most frequently transmitted to a mechanical recording lever; although for photographic recording a mirror is sometimes mounted on the diaphragm or operated by the diaphragm.

A very important requirement of such air-pressure devices is that the record made by them be linearly related to the changes in air pressure. This is sometimes difficult to obtain. For example, a simple rubber diaphragm will respond more to a unit change in pressure when that diaphragm is loose than it will when it is taut. A resulting record will show lack of linearity between pressure changes and recorder response, a situation which may be reduced by using special diaphragm rubber. Where linearity is an essential requirement, devices other than tambours have advantages. Two of the most common of these are piston recorders and bellows recorders (Fig. 2 - 6b and c).

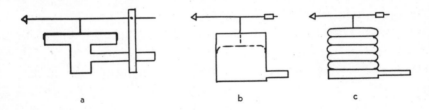

a   b   c

Fig. 2 - 6—Diagrams of pressure recorders: (a) tambour, (b) piston recorder, (c) bellows recorder

The piston recorder is constructed like the piston in a conventional air pump with the lever mounted on the piston proper and an intake valve at the base of the cylinder. Changes in air pressure slide the piston up and down in the cylinder. Bellows recorders are similar in construction to an accordion, such that an increase in pressure linearly expands the folds of the bellows (Fig. 2 - 7).

In many situations it is necessary to reduce the pressure in a pneumatic system before that pressure is applied to a tambour. For example, in the typical human blood-pressure recording with a *sphygmomanometer,* sufficient pressure is built up in a band around the subject's arm to equal arterial blood pressure. If this pressure were applied to an ordinary tambour, the diaphragm would be forced out. For such purposes a tambour specialized for high pressure may be utilized; or an intermediate device may be employed for reducing the pressure before it is applied to an ordinary tambour. Such a pressure-reducing device usually consists of two airtight chambers separated by a fairly heavy diaphragm. One chamber, at high pressure, leads directly to the system under observation. Changes in pressure in this chamber are communicated by means of the diaphragm into low pressure changes in the second chamber which leads directly to the recording tambour.

Tambours and allied devices have two major adjustments. One, for centering, alters the initial position of the lever with reference to the diaphragm. The second changes the distance from the fulcrum to the point of application of force on the lever, thereby controlling the magnification ratio. In addition, tambours may be provided with a pressure escape valve which may be opened while preliminary adjustments are being made.

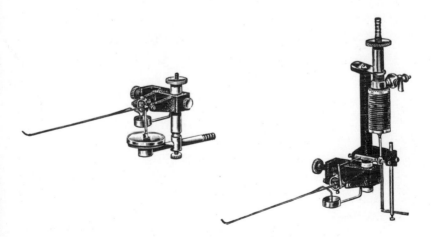

Fig. 2 - 7—Tambour and bellows recorders. (Courtesy Phipps & Bird, Inc., Richmond, Va.)

Bellows and membrane manometers are also employed for measuring liquid pressure systems. The membranes and diaphragm surfaces are considerably reduced in size to permit higher pressures, and a bleeding valve is provided for letting out air and excess liquid. A very common type of laboratory manometer is the mercury, or gravity-type, device. It consists of a U-tube partially filled with mercury (Fig. 2 - 8a). One side of the tube communicates with the system being recorded.

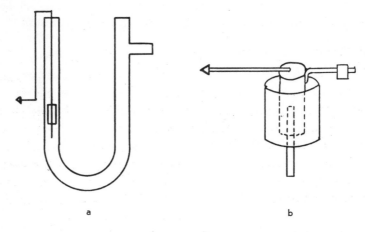

a   b

Fig. 2 - 8—(a) Mercury manometer, (b) float-type volume recorder

Pressure changes alter the position of the mercury in the tube, and these changes are recorded by a stylus which is mounted in a float riding on top of the mercury in the other side of the tube. The float is ordinarily concave to fit the mercury meniscus and is stabilized by a wire extending a short distance into the mercury.

Volume Recorders

Sometimes it is necessary to record changes in the volume of a liquid system, as, for example, in the study of blood-volume

changes in the extremities of the body during emotional experience. In this case a device termed a *plethysmograph* might be
used. The changes in the gross volume of a member of the body
(i.e., the arm) are picked up by encasing the arm in a liquid-
filled container and converting variations in liquid level to variations in air pressure in a tambour for registration. Or a second device of this class, the *float recorder* (Fig. 2 - 8b), might
be used. The liquid of the system under observation is led directly into a vessel. Within the vessel a float rides on top of the
liquid, and changes in level of the liquid are communicated to
the recording surface by a stylus mounted on the float.

ELECTROMAGNETIC MARKERS

Frequently it is necessary only to indicate the beginning
and cessation of an event, or to record the on-off occurrences
of an electric circuit. Such a recording is made by an electromagnetic marker, or *signal magnet*. This in its simplest form
contains a small solenoid which becomes an electromagnet when
a current is passed through it. The magnet attracts the reed of
a recording lever, pulling it across the recording surface. When
the current through the coil is stopped, the magnet releases the
reed and a spring returns it to its original position (Fig. 2 - 9).
In its more complicated form, a signal magnet may record two

Fig. 2 - 9—Signal magnets

or more systems with a single stylus by having more than one set of magnets, and having one set pull the reed up while the other set pulls the reed down.

Oscillographs

Whenever one wishes to record oscillations in an electrical system, it is necessary to have a device which will indicate not only the on-off relationship but also the direction and the amount of current or voltage change. A picture of such an electrical wave form is termed an *oscillogram,* and the term *oscillograph* is used to refer to the device which registers the picture.

One form of oscillograph employs the principle of the *moving-coil galvanometer.* A small coil of wire is suspended between opposed magnetic poles. When a current is passed through the coil, a magnetic field is set up which interacts with the first magnetic field. This exerts a torque on the coil causing it to turn on its axis to align itself with the magnetic poles. The amount of turn, and the return of the coil, is controlled by elastic tensions in the suspension mechanism of the coil. The movements in the coil are transmitted to the recording surface by means of a mirror or a pointer attached to the coil (Fig. 2 - 10).

Another common oscillograph works on the same basic principle as the above and is termed by many a moving-coil oscillograph. Since its structure is slightly different from the above, and it is patterned after the so-called dynamic loud speakers used in radio (Fig. 2 - 11), it is sometimes termed an *electrodynamic oscillograph.* A coil of fine wire is wound on a light cylindrical paper core. This is then suspended around the pole piece of an electromagnet. When a current passes through the coil, the coil becomes an electromagnet. The resulting interaction of magnetic fields of the stationary magnet and the coil causes the coil to move along the pole piece. If a mirror or stylus is attached to the coil, the movement of the coil may be registered on a recording surface. Considerable latitude in the construction of such devices is possible, for the stationary

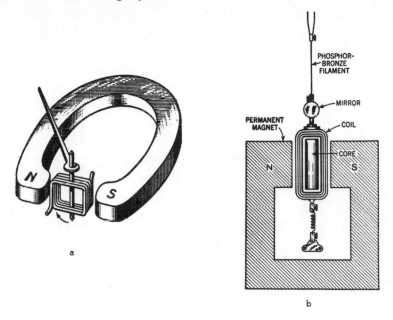

Fig. 2 - 10—Moving-coil galvanometers. (By permission from *Fundamentals of electricity*, by Carnegie-Illinois Steel Corp., 1943, American Book Co.)

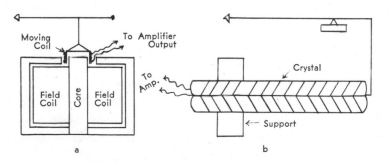

Fig. 2 - 11—Two forms of electric oscillographs:
(a) moving-coil "electrodynamic," (b) crystal

magnet may be made weak or strong, an electromagnet or a permanent magnet.

The moving-coil principle is used in many diversified oscillographic applications. When a mirror is mounted on the coil, or on a reed attached to the coil, an efficient optical lever capable of fairly high frequencies may be constructed. Most recent applications involving moderately slow frequencies of oscillation (to about 100 cps as in electroencephalography) use ink-writing modifications built like small motors. One commercial instrument of this type is called a "Penmotor" (5). It is made of a rotary moving coil in a uniform field of high flux density. Special design considerations (a doubly resonant system) are made to extend the frequency response range.

A simple and useful class of *magnetic oscillographs* depends for its action not upon an interaction of magnetic fields, as in the above, but upon the varying degrees of attraction of a changing magnetic field for a soft iron diaphragm or armature. This is the principle of common headphones, telephone receivers, and early forms of radio speakers. The essential element is a soft-iron diaphragm or armature placed in the field of an electromagnet. The armature, to which the stylus is attached, is variously attracted to the electromagnet depending upon the changes in the magnetic field, which in turn are due to the fluctuation in current from the system being recorded. One of the disadvantages of this type of oscillograph is that, in order to maintain linear response, only small angular changes can be employed. This requires lever amplification systems.

A very sensitive device for small current changes, capable of considerable optical magnification, is the *string galvanometer*. It is based on the principle, similar to the above, that when a current is passed through a wire, a magnetic field is set up around the wire. If this wire lies in a magnetic field when a current is passed through it, the wire will be moved out of its position due to the interaction of the magnetic fields. The typical string galvanometer consists of a fine-drawn conductor thread mounted between pole pieces of a powerful electromagnet. Currents to be recorded pass through the string, and the resulting interaction of magnetic fields bows the string or pulls it away from its central position. Registration of the changes in the position of the string are accomplished by an optical magnification and photographic system of the photokymograph type.

Another oscillograph is based on the principle that certain *crystals* (Rochelle salts, for example) are altered in shape by a potential difference between their two sides. A potential change applied to such a crystal will result in a change in the surface of the crystal. These changes may be communicated by means of a lever system to a recording surface (Fig. 2 - 11).

The *cathode-ray oscillograph* consists of a cathode-ray tube with auxiliary circuits to control beam characteristics, and supplementary circuits to amplify signals and provide a time base (sweep). (See Fig. 2 - 12.) It has advantages over all other oscillographs in some respects. It is free of inertia effects; there are no limitations on the frequency of response; and com-

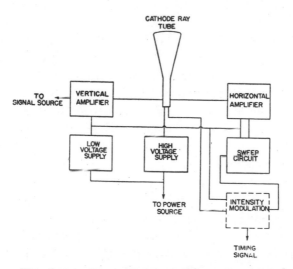

Fig. 2 - 12—Block diagram of the cathode-ray oscillograph. (Courtesy Allen B. Du Mont Labs., Inc., Passaic, N. J.)

plicated patterns of response may be registered simultaneously. Its one practical disadvantage is that, where lengthy permanent records are required, specialized photographic recording is necessary.

The cathode-ray tube is a specialized electron tube. Its outstanding feature is that an electron beam is made visible through a fluorescent screen. By means of this beam of electrons, the tube is able to portray visually a great many electrical phenomena. The general structure of such a tube may be considered in a simplified illustration (Fig. 2 - 13). In this diagram the tube may be compared to a typical radio tube with

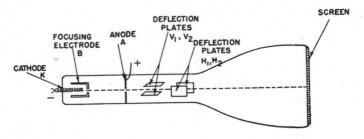

Fig. 2 - 13—Simplified illustration of a cathode-ray tube

a cathode giving off electrons and a plate (anode) with high positive potential pulling those electrons toward it. If there were a small hole in the plate, a stream of electrons would pass through the plate and strike the fluorescent screen at the end of the tube, thus producing a light spot. Since this beam of electrons which passes through the hole would behave as any other group of electrons, it would be possible to alter its course by exerting magnetic or electrostatic forces upon it. This would cause the visible spot to move about on the screen.

Such a controlling influence over the course of an electron beam can be achieved by adding electrostatic (charged) plates into the tube in a position such that, when a particular plate bears a positive charge, the beam is attracted (bent) toward it. If two pairs of such plates are placed in the tube, one pair in the vertical plane and the other in the horizontal plane, and with one plate of each pair on either side of the beam, it becomes possible, through the application of appropriate charges to the plates, to deflect the electron beam (and the resulting spot) in any direction.

The function of the various accessory circuits to the cathode-ray tube may be summarized by considering the control panel (Fig. 2 - 14) and the adjustments which result from each control.

The *intensity* adjustment controls the number of electrons in the beam and therefore the brightness of the visible image. This is accomplished by varying the voltage on the control grid of the tube. The *focus* determines the sharpness or fineness of the beam. This is made possible by the inclusion of more than one plate or anode in the tube. Varying the potential difference between the anodes creates an electrostatic "squeeze" effect upon the beam. The *centering controls* alter the location of the beam or pattern on the screen. The vertical centering knob moves the spot or patterns up or down, and the horizontal centering adjustment moves it right or left. Such position shifts are brought about by the introduction of slight DC potentials to the appropriate deflection plates.

The vertical amplifier input is a terminal for introducing external signal voltages to the vertical deflection plates (movement in the vertical axis). It leads into the high-gain vertical amplifier, where degree of amplification is adjusted by the gain or amplitude control. The horizontal amplifier input signal terminal and the horizontal amplifier have the same general role for the horizontal plates except that the voltage gain of the amplifier is usually less than that on the vertical plates.

These basic controls regulate the electron beam in its resting position and permit the portrayal of certain limited forms of electrical impulses applied to the deflection plates. In the case of an alternating potential applied to the vertical set of plates, these adjustments give control only over the *amplitude* characteristics of the wave pattern; for the amount of deflec-

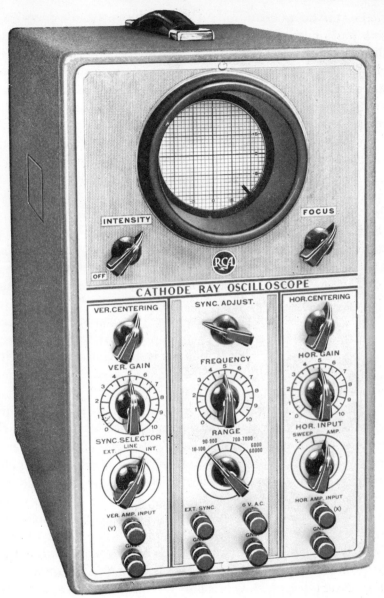

Fig. 2 - 14—The control panel of a cathode-ray oscillograph. (Courtesy Radio Corporation of America, Camden, N. J.)

tion of the beam above its resting point corresponds to the positive portion of the cycle, and the amount of deflection below the resting point corresponds to the negative portion of the cycle. In the usual analysis of alternating currents and complex wave forms it is desirable to portray two dimensions, *amplitude* and *frequency*. The frequency dimension requires the addition of some form of time base to the above amplitude controls.

This is accomplished by the introduction of a *sweep circuit* which causes a *sweep signal* to be applied to one of the sets of plates (usually the horizontal). This sweep signal causes the spot to move across the screen (usually from left to right) at a definite temporal rate. The *sweep frequency controls* regulate the rate at which the spot will cross the screen and return to its starting point. Coarse and fine frequency controls are provided. The coarse adjustment determines the general range of sweep frequencies, and the fine frequency control determines the specific frequency within that range.

PICKUP DEVICES

MECHANICAL

The simplest device for picking up observed movement couples the moving system directly and mechanically with the registration lever. For example, a measure of finger tremor may use a light stylus attached to the finger; the resulting movements of the stylus then interrupt light in a photorecorder (or perhaps a photoelectric cell), or the stylus may register directly on the surface of a kymograph drum. Blinking of the eye in eyelid conditioning may be communicated by a lever attached directly to the eyelid. Movements of the finger in a typical finger ergograph are communicated directly to a recording surface. Examples of such pickup are numerous. An important requirement is that they do not in any way alter the system being recorded in the sense of influencing it or acting back upon it—a requirement which holds for all pickup devices.

PNEUMATIC PICKUP

Transposing behavioral changes into air-pressure changes in a pneumatic system is a common practice. A *pneumograph,* for example, is a pickup device for detecting breathing changes. It consists of a hollow corrugated rubber tube which is placed around the chest of the person being observed (Fig. 2 - 15).

Fig. 2 - 15 — Different types of pneumographs. (Courtesy Phipps & Bird, Inc., Richmond, Va.)

Expansion and contraction of the chest during breathing change the tension on the rubber tube, which in turn alters the air pressure within the tube. These changes are transmitted by an outlet valve to a registration device such as a tambour. The *sphygmomanometer* is a pneumatic device for picking up the heart beat and changes in blood pressure. In its common form a flat air-bladder is wrapped around the subject's arm and air is introduced in this bladder until a pressure is reached which will just counteract the arterial blood pressure. Pressure level may be read from the dial of a pressure meter; or changes in pressure, such as occur with each beat of the heart or with stimulation, may be transmitted to a kymographic registration device.

Pneumatic pickup systems are often employed in the general class of apparatus known as *stabilimeters.* A stabilimeter is a device for detecting small changes in equilibrium or general movement; as, for example, in studying the amounts of general activity of a newborn infant. In this example, a platform on which the infant rests could be mounted on springs. The springs would be of such a tension as to respond to appropriate movements of the platform (according to the sensitivity desired). Rubber tubes placed around the springs could make intact pneumatic systems, such that movements in the platform become transformed into air displacements in a tambour. These are only a few of the applications of pneumatic pickup devices.

SIMPLE ELECTRIC CONTACT

The indication of movement, or the beginning and end of an event, is commonly accomplished by an electric contact which is manually or mechanically operated. The most familiar example of this type is the telegraph key in reaction-time experiments. Another is the stylus in a tapping test which, when brought in contact with a contact plate, completes the circuit to an electric counter. In the familiar rotary pursuit test, or pursuitmeter, the time that the subject is on the target is recorded by the contact between the stylus and the metal target on a revolving disk—the circuit to an electric timer being completed when the stylus is in contact with the disk.

PICKUP POTENTIOMETERS

A device which permits electrical indication not only of the starting and stopping of a movement but also amount of movement consists essentially of a slide wire resistor connected in such a way that the system under observation controls the slider. Changes in the position of the slider or wiper alters the resistance of an external recording system. These changes may be registered as resultant current changes in a meter or as potential changes in an oscillograph. This general concept of resistance-coupled pickup device is very common, for it is the same principle embodied in some microphone pickups and in some photoelectric cell pickups.

MICROPHONES

In some form or another microphonic pickup devices are used in a large number of situations. The most common form is in picking up sound. Other forms include direct coupling of a moving system to the microphone diaphragm as in the case of tremor measurement or recording of heart beat; or pneumatic coupling may be used to transform an air-pressure system into an electric system by means of microphones.

There are many types of microphones available for use in the laboratory (Fig. 2 - 16). One of these, the *carbon microphone,* consists of a small button filled with tiny carbon gran-

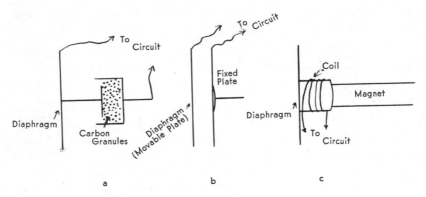

Fig. 2 - 16—Common microphones: (a) carbon-button, (b) condenser, (c) moving-coil

ules. One side of the button is fixed, the other is movable and communicates directly with the diaphragm. Movements of the diaphragm either compress or loosen the granules and in this way change the contact resistance between the granules. Since the two sides of the button are connected in a series circuit, the resulting changes in resistance through the button are transmitted to the circuit.

A similar principle is embodied in the *condenser microphone.* This consists of a condenser with one plate rigid and the other plate movable in harmony with a diaphragm. Movement of the diaphragm changes the distance of the movable plate of the condenser from the fixed plate of the condenser. This, in turn, is reflected by altered capacitance of the condenser since such capacitance depends upon the thickness of the dielectric—in this case the separation of the two plates. Therefore, the diaphragm movements produce changes in the electrical circuit of which the condenser is a part.

A moving-coil or *electrodynamic microphone* is based on the principle of induction. A small coil of wire attached to a diaphragm passes over the end of the pole piece of a magnet. Movement of the diaphragm back and forth causes the coil to cut lines of force in the magnetic field. As a result, a current which varies with the number of lines of force cut, hence with the rate of vibration of the diaphragm, is generated in the coil. A special type of electrodynamic microphone substitutes a very thin, flexible corrugated aluminum ribbon for the coil. As it vibrates in the magnetic field, a voltage is generated between its ends. This is often referred to as a *velocity microphone.*

One of the most common in laboratory work is the *crystal microphone.* It is based on the principle that when a force is applied to certain crystals (Rochelle salts or quartz) a voltage difference appears between their two sides. The amplitude of the voltage generated is proportional, within limits, to the force applied. Both the crystal and electrodynamic type microphones require no separate source of current—that is, they generate a potential. The other types operate as resistances in a circuit. A much less common device is a *vacuum-tube microphone* (mechanoelectric transducer) which consists of a three-element electron tube with a diaphragm to which the control grid is connected. Movement of the control grid with vibrations of the diaphragm alters the plate current of the tube.

VOICE KEYS

One of the common applications of microphones is in indicating a verbal response, as, for example, in the measurement of a verbal reaction time. A simplified diagram of such

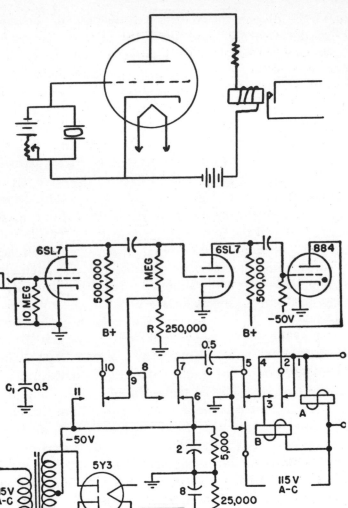

Fig. 2 - 17—Voice keys. (Top) Simplified diagram of a microphone-operated relay; (bottom) a complete voice-key circuit. (By permission from *Handbook of industrial electronic circuits*, by Markus and Zeluff, 1948, McGraw-Hill Book Co.; courtesy *Electronics*)

an electronic voice key is shown in Figure 2 - 17. The carbon microphone operates as a resistance in a grid circuit. When a word is spoken, the resistance of the microphone is reduced, the grid becomes more positive, more plate current flows, and the relay in the plate circuit is energized completing the external circuit through the registration device. Some voice keys operate on a simple contact principle in which vibrations of an aluminum membrane interrupt current through a platinum contact.

STRAIN GAGES

The influence of stress within a material such as wire upon the resistance of the material has led to special pickup devices termed *strain gages* (6). The essential feature of these instruments is a fine metal wire mounted in a multiple-W form on paper and cemented to the part under test. The wire undergoes a change in resistance proportional to the strain upon it. The resistance change occurs because the stress on the wire makes that conductor longer and thinner. The resistance change may then be amplified electronically for registration with an oscillograph.

ELECTRODES

In instances in which the observed phenomena involve potential changes in or on the body electrodes of various sorts may be applied to the body surface or inserted into the bodily tissues. Examples include picking up potential charges generated in the body, such as muscle and nerve action potentials; or measuring resistance changes on the body surface, as in the galvanic skin response. There are numerous problems in the use of such electrodes. The most important of these are polarization and the setting up of little voltaic cells at points of contact. These problems will be discussed in more detail in connection with bioelectric measurement.

CHANGES IN LIGHT OUTPUT

It is often desirable to transform changes in light output to changes in electrical potential for conveniences of amplification and registration. This is most frequently accomplished by means of photoelectric cells. The light wave changes incident upon the photosensitive cell result in electrical variations in an external circuit. These electrical changes are usually recorded oscillographically.

There are three major classes of photoelectric cells: (1) *photoemissive* cells, (2) *photoconductive* cells, and (3) *photovoltaic* cells. Photoemissive cells are electronic tubes, either evacuated or gas filled. Electrons are emitted by a metallic (cold) cathode when that element is exposed to light. These electrons are then collected upon a plate or anode maintained at a positive potential by an external source. Fluctuations in light result in fluctuations in current through the tube. Since the current is in the order of microamperes, it is ordinarily necessary to employ vacuum-tube amplifiers. Photovoltaic cells are the only other class to see wide use in psychology. They are small electric generators, for a transfer of electrons across the rectifying boundary of certain substances occurs when light falls upon the material. The most common application of these cells is in portable instruments for measuring light intensity.

TEMPERATURE CHANGES

It may be necessary to record or control temperature as a variable in an investigation. Such temperature changes can be picked up through the application of thermal properties of certain substances. Perhaps the commonest is the *thermostat* arrangement based on differing rates of expansion of different metals. Two metals with different rates of expansion are joined into a unit. With a change in temperature, and a resultant greater expansion of one part than of the other, the shape of the unit is altered. This change in shape may complete a circuit activating a relay or other control device. Less common examples are based on the principles that junctions of dissimilar metals generate a current when heated and that resistance of some material to the passage of an electric current varies with temperature (7).

SOME COMMERCIAL RECORDERS

INK-WRITING AMMETERS AND VOLTMETERS

An example of a direct ink-recording milliammeter is shown in Figure 2 - 18. The manufacturer is the Esterline Angus Co. of Indianapolis, Ind. This instrument consists of a mov-

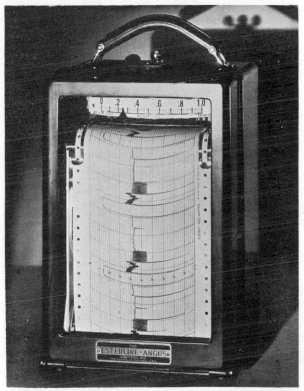

Fig. 2 - 18—A direct-writing milliammeter. (Courtesy Esterline-Angus Co., Indianapolis, Ind.)

ing-coil milliammeter with a light capillary pen mounted on the coil. The measuring element is shown in Figure 2 - 19. One end of the pen communicates with an ink reservoir. The second

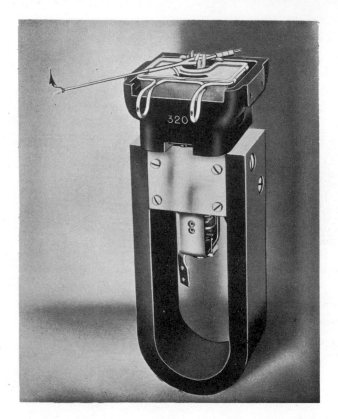

Fig. 2 - 19—The d'Arsonval measuring element employed in the recorder in Figure 2 - 18

major portion of the instrument is the chart drive, usually operated by a synchronous motor. Various chart speeds, many forms of lined and unlined charts, and portable and stationary cases are obtainable. The meter element may be obtained without the chart drive for use with other polygraphs.

Oscillographs

The commercial oscillograph is similar in general structure to the above device except that it is adapted to the recording of more rapidly changing systems by the substitution of an
ink-writing oscillograph for the meter element. For example,
the instrument illustrated above is adapted to follow as many
as 10 "on-off" cycles per second, whereas the oscillograph in
Figure 2 - 20 is linear to nearly 100 cps. The two types of instruments are designed to satisfy different requirements—
the former to achieve maximum sensitivity and pen swing on
slowly changing systems, the latter to preserve linear response
at higher frequences. The difference can be seen readily in
typical psychological applications. Ink-writing meters, such
as that in Figure 2 - 18, are specially adapted to the measurement of the galvanic skin response, while oscillographs similar
to that in Figure 2 - 20 are necessary in electroencephalography. The oscillograph element illustrated is the Penmotor, discussed earlier in reference to registration devices. Photographic
oscillographs, similar to that in Figure 2 - 21, permit recording even higher rates of oscillation (4,000 - 5,000 cps).

Photoelectric Recorders

A device capable, in the manufacturer's words, of "recording anything that can be measured," extends the range of the
direct-writing meter element by introducing an optical followup system for developing the power necessary to operate a recording pen. A diagram of how such a device operates is given
in Figure 2 - 22.

The basic element responding to the system being observed is a galvanometer of the moving-coil type with a mirror
attached to the coil. The condensed light from an incandescent
bulb falls on this mirror and is reflected to a spherical mirror,
then to a mirror extending from the coil of a moving-coil element which forms the pen-driving element. The light reflect-

Fig. 2-20—A six-pen oscillograph. The inset shows individual mountings of the pen elements. (Courtesy Brush Development Co., Cleveland, O.)

Fig. 2 - 21—A photographic oscillograph. (Courtesy Hathaway Instrument Co., Denver, Colorado)

ing from this mirror falls upon a light-dividing mirror which divides it between two phototubes.

As long as the mirrors of the basic element and the pen element are parallel, the light will be divided equally between the phototubes and the circuit controlled by these cells will be balanced. The recording element will receive current only when the phototube balance is upset. For example, when the pen is slightly to the left of its correct position for the setting of the basic element mirror, a greater portion of light will fall on the far phototube. This will cause a current to flow through the coil of the recording element such as to move the pen to the right. The optical followup system, a servomechanism, permits considerable amplification. The rated sensitivities of the instrument described range from one microampere full scale with a period of about four seconds to the order of milliamperes with frequency rates to five per second.

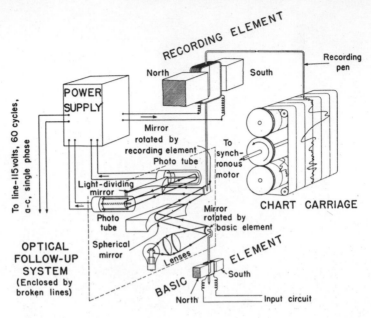

Fig. 2 - 22—A photoelectric recorder (schematic diagram of how it works). (Courtesy General Electric Co., Schenectady, N. Y.)

Special Polygraphs and Kymographs

One of the most common multipurpose recorders in psychological use is that which combines the measurement of breathing, heart rate, blood pressure, and the galvanic skin response. An example of this type is shown in Figure 2 - 23 with all of its pickup devices. It employs ink-writing capillary pens. Another common polygraph, the chronograph, is specialized for receiving a time line. An example of this type was shown in Figure 2 - 4 and a different view (top) is given in Figure 2 - 24.

Kymographic recording cameras are also available commercially. They range from cylindrical lens photokymographs to specialized cameras for recording the traces on the screen

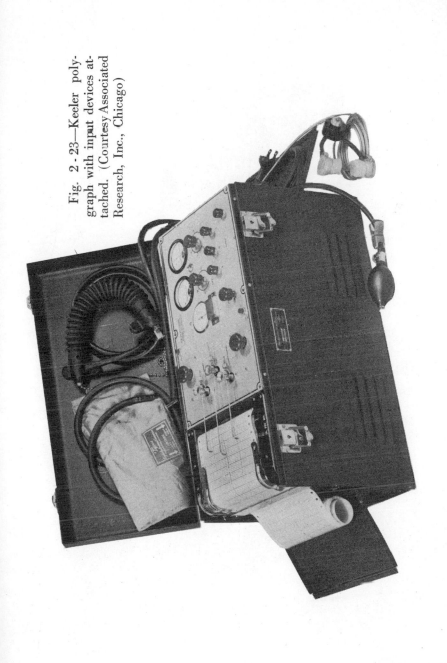

Fig. 2 - 23—Keeler polygraph with input devices attached. (Courtesy Associated Research, Inc., Chicago)

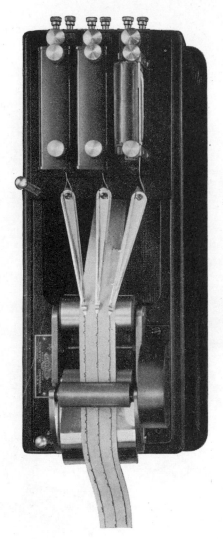

Fig. 2-24—Top view of a chronograph registering data. (Courtesy Gaertner Scientific Corp., Chicago, Ill.)

Fig. 2 - 25—Cathode-ray oscillograph camera. (Courtesy Allen B. Du Mont Labs., Inc., Passaic, N. J.)

of a cathode-ray oscillograph (Fig 2 - 25) or for photographing the movements of the eyes during reading.

CHARACTERISTICS OF A GOOD RECORDING SYSTEM

Sensitivity and Range

It is essential that a recorder be capable of detecting, transmitting, and registering all aspects of the observed system which are relevant to later data analysis. Its sensitivity must be sufficient to detect the smallest change that needs to be recorded. At the same time, sensitivity must not be so great as to pick up irrelevant, undesirable, and possibly interfering changes. Appropriate sensitivity rather than high sensitivity is to be desired. Closely allied to sensitivity is the problem of covering a sufficiently wide range of recorded responses that each response, whether large or small, gets an appropriate place on the recording surface. To a large degree, sensitivity and range are reciprocally related, for as sensitivity increases, range decreases and vice versa. A practical solution must be reached in which the recorder is capable of picking up all necessary changes within the range of the system being observed.

RELIABILITY

A good recording system introduces a minimum of variability into a record. Two main sources of such variability are distortion and equipment variation. Both of these factors are involved in the reliability of an instrument. A recorder must be consistent in the sense of giving the same measurement on repeated occasions (assuming that the system being measured has not changed).

Distortion may act as either a constant or a variable error. If it operates as a constant error, correction can often be made for the fact by means of conversion tables and statistical controls. Many sources of error in a recorder operate in both directions—in other words, they introduce variable errors. The assumption that such errors are random often is not justified. Variable errors are typically related to electrical or mechanical weaknesses in a device and for this reason may operate more frequently in one direction than in another—even though they do not work consistently in that direction. Such variation introduced by the apparatus may be of sufficient magnitude to completely mask observed results, or to lead to erroneous conclusions.

BACKWARD ACTION

If a recording device operates to effect or alter in some way the system being observed, that recorder is "acting back" upon the observed phenomenon. Such an influence of recorder upon the system being recorded must be avoided. An example of such backward action might occur in the recording of eyeblink response by means of a stylus attached to the eyelid. If the stylus were heavy enough to interfere with the normal operation of the eyelid, backward action would result, and any data collected from such a system would be subject to an unknown amount of variation.

INERTIA FACTORS

Particularly with reference to the functioning of registration devices, inertia may contribute to distortion. Two major evidences of inertia are seen in *lag* and *overshoot* of recording levers. A lever which is too heavy or too long will not respond immediately to a force applied to it; it will not respond until sufficient force has been applied to overcome its standing inertia. Such a slow takeoff of a lever, or slow response to change, is termed lag. Such a lever, once it gets moving, will strongly resist being stopped. The result is that it continues to move after the movement in the system has ceased—it overshoots. Control of lag and overshoot is most directly achieved when careful attention is paid to inertia factors in the construction of a lever system (namely: weight, length, and magnification ratio); special care in construction to prevent loose and wobbly, or very tight and binding couplings; and application of appropriate friction to counteract those difficulties which may not be otherwise eliminated. The application of such friction is termed *damping*.

NATURAL VIBRATION

Levers have a rate of vibration which is characteristic of them. This represents a rate at which they will vibrate in their natural state. There will also be certain resonant frequencies at which they will more readily vibrate than at others. If a lever system has an inherent vibration rate which is less than the oscillation rate of the system being recorded, the resulting record will have the faster rate superimposed on the slower rate and will be subject to summation and interference effects between the two rates. The results will be distortion in amplitude.

If the natural rate of vibration of the registration device is much higher than that of the observed system, these difficulties are much reduced, for the slower movements will be superimposed on the rapid movements in such a way that, when the difference in the two frequencies is great, there will be no appreciable effect on the record by oscillations in the registration device. A good general rule with reference to recording levers is to insure that the natural vibration rate of the lever is much higher than that of the recorded system. The chief factors determining natural rate of vibration are mass, elasticity, and friction. In many instances, it is possible to damp out all natural vibrations by increasing frictional factors.

ARCING ERRORS

Recording levers operating about a fulcrum point will inscribe an arc on the final record. Levers which are attached directly to a recorded system without such a pivotal point will move directly in or out, up or down, etc. In some cases, both kinds of tracings (one from a lever operating in an arc, another from a linearly operating lever) may appear on the same record. In all cases, it is essential to be aware of certain distortion introduced by the arc-type lever, and to make allowances for this arcing error when the records are analyzed. In terms of amplitude, or magnitude of response measure, the arcing stylus consistently gives a smaller response than does a rectangular recording stylus. Some of the height of the tracing is lost in the turning operation. Time errors may be similarly introduced when time reference is made to the "long" axis of the record. Different positions of the stylus (with reference to its total arc) are above different points on the base line at the same instant of time. This makes the reading of comparative times of several arcing styli difficult. To make correction for these difficulties easier, recording papers are available with curved grid lines of different radii of curvature.

REFERENCES

1. WENDT, G. R. Methods of recording action, *Arch. psychol.*, 1938, No. 228, p. 83.
2. HALEY, T. J. A solution for plasticizing kymograph records, *Science*, 1947, 106, 350.
3. LEWIS, L. W. A simple pen for kymograph tracings, *Science*, 1947, 106, 451.
4. GERBRANDS, R., and VOLKMANN, J. A wax paper kymograph, *Amer. j. psychol.*, 1936, 48, 498-501.
5. SHAPER, II. B. Electrodynamic direct inking pen, *Electronics*, 1946, 19, No. 3, 148-151.
6. DOBIE, W. B., and ISAAC, C. G. *Electric resistance strain gauges.* New York: Macmillan, 1949.
7. STOLL, A. M., and HARDY, J. D. Temperature: measuring devices. P. 1112-1117 in Glasser, O. *Medical physics.* Vol. 2. Chicago: Year Book Publishing Co., 1950.
8. MARKUS, J., and ZELUFF, V. *Handbook of industrial electronic circuits.* New York: McGraw-Hill Book Co., Inc., 1948.
9. DAVIS, R. C. Methods of measuring and recording action. Chap. 14, in ANDREWS, T. G. (ed.) *Methods of psychology.* New York: John Wiley and Sons, Inc., 1948.

CHAPTER 3

Timing and Counting

TIMING APPARATUS

There are two major problems to be solved by timing apparatus. One is to measure exactly intervals of time. The other is to control the factor of time as a variable in an experiment. The most extensive applications of time measurement devices in psychology are in the study of response latencies and response patterns. The most extensive applications of time-control devices are for the control of stimulus duration and patterns of stimuli. Examples of specialization for measurement are seen in the stop watch, the chronograph, and the chronoscope. Specialized equipment for time control are usually called timers and examples are time markers and interval timers.

It is not easy to separate instruments according to their function as control and measurement devices, for many of them serve both functions. Most devices fall into five or six major classes according to their fundamental principles of operation, and both measurement and control applications may exist in each class. The material which follows, therefore, is discussed from a dual frame of reference: fundamental principles of operation and major function.

CHRONOSCOPES: HISTORICAL

As a class, *chronoscopes* are designed to provide accurate measurement of temporal intervals. Many of the older types are no longer used for research purposes but are frequently present in psychological laboratories and used to demonstrate basic principles. Some examples of these older instruments are shown in Figure 3 - 1. The *vernier chronoscope* calculates

50

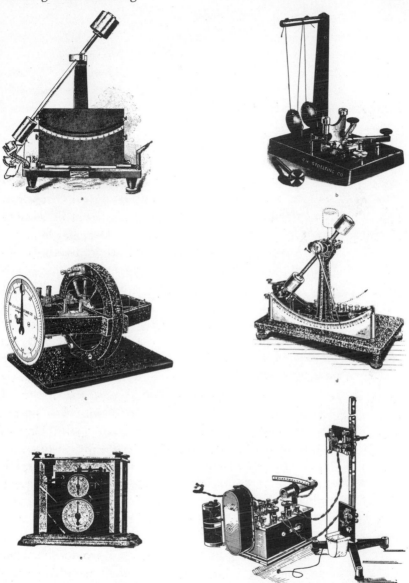

Fig. 3 - 1—Chronoscopes of historical interest: (a) Seashore spark pendulum, (b) vernier chronoscope, (c) John Hopkins synchronous motor, (d) Bergstrom pendulum, (e) Hipp clock, (f) Klopsteg galvanometer with fall apparatus. (Courtesy C. H. Stoelting Co., Chicago)

elapsed time from the difference in periods of a pair of unequal pendulums, by counting the number of swings it takes a faster swinging pendulum started at the end of an interval to catch up with a slower (longer) pendulum started at the beginning of the interval. The *Hipp* and *d'Arsonval clocks* are essentially spring clocks constructed to tick in thousandths of a second. The speed of the driving mechanism is governed by a vibrating reed operating on the teeth of a balance wheel. They are equipped with a device for clutching indicator hands in and out. Various *pendulum chronoscopes* are best known by the names of the persons using them, such as Bergstrom, Seashore, Hathaway, and Dodge—the last is described below. Two other classes, *synchronous motor chronoscopes*, such as the John Hopkins, and *galvanometer chronoscopes*, such as Klopsteg's, have modern versions which are discussed below.

Pendulum Chronoscopes and Chronographs

The *Dodge photochronograph* (Fig. 3 - 2) is illustrative of pendulum time measurement and control devices. It was originally designed to provide simulational and recording apparatus for eyelid conditioning (1). The apparatus consists of a long pendulum mounted on bearings. The arc traversed by the bob is paralleled by a similar arc on the base of the apparatus on which are mounted rotary switches or contact plates adjustable in distance along the arc. In its typical control operation, the pendulum is released automatically by a magnetic mechanism; as the pendulum strikes the first switch the conditioned stimulus is turned on; as the second switch is struck, the unconditioned stimulus is turned on; and when the third switch is hit, both the unconditioned and conditioned stimuli are turned off. Frequently a fourth switch resets the switches and prepares the pendulum automatically for the next trial.

As chronoscopes, pendulum devices compute elapsed time from velocity and acceleration of the bob during any phase of its arc. In the case of the Dodge, the pendulum has a section of photographic paper mounted on the pendulum which passes a

Fig. 3 - 2—A modified Dodge time pendulum equipped with rotary switches

lighted aperture during the arc. The onset and end of the stimu-
lus-response interval are registered by shadow-casting devices,
and the time between them is computed from the distance between marks on the recording paper. This arrangement is most
appropriately termed a chronograph. Other pendulum devices
register sparks at various points on the arc, or have electrically
operated indicators which are held fast at a point in the arc,
thereby indicating elapsed time. For the most part these instruments have gone out of use, being supplanted by synchronous
motor and electronic devices.

SYNCHRONOUS MOTOR CLOCKS

The most common time-measuring devices used for research in psychological laboratories are electric stop clocks.
The essential elements of such clocks are a synchronous motor

which runs continuously and an electrically controlled clutching mechanism for starting and stopping the hands. These electric time clocks are available in a large range of sensitivities and scale units. Some manufacturers make models for short time measurement that are accurate to within .5 sigma, although less accurate, and consequently less expensive, models are more often used. Most types contain provision for manual starting and stopping and for operation of the clutch mechanism by an external electrical circuit. Different current and voltage constants for the clutches are available to make the clocks adaptable to most laboratory time-measuring applications.

A popular example of these stop clocks is the Standard Electric Time Company model illustrated in Figure 3 - 3. The clock motor runs continuously when the clock is connected, and a relatively simple friction-type clutch starts and stops the

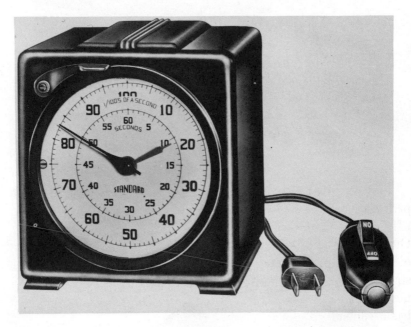

Fig. 3 - 3—A synchronous-motor stop clock. (Courtesy
Standard Electric Time Co., Springfield, Mass.)

hands (Fig 3·4). The motor drive shaft ends in a grooved
wheel (GW) which is friction coupled (at F) with a spring
hook (SH) to the indicator driving mechanism. On the hand-
driving mechanism is a flywheel (FW) which revolves with
the hand. A brake lever (B) is operated by a relay (R). When
no current is flowing through the relay, the brake is held by
spring tension against the flywheel. This causes the spring hook
to slide over the grooved wheel at the friction joint (F), and the
hands of the clock remain stationary. When the clutch circuit
is completed, current flows through the relay coil, the brake is
lifted, and the friction joint drives the hands.

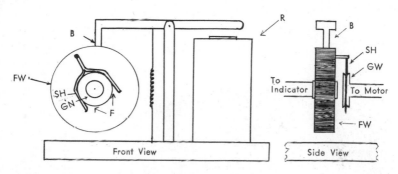

Fig. 3 - 4—Drawing of clock clutch mechanism showing: (R)
relay, (B) brake, (FW) flywheel, (SH) spring hook, (F) friction
coupling, (GW) grooved wheel on motor drive shaft

These clocks are particularly useful when they are equipped with auxiliary electronic devices for turning them on and
off. They can readily be operated acoustically by a voice key.
Or electrical pulses such as might be generated by a photoelectric cell pickup may be used to operate the clutch. An instrument for controlling such a clock by both video and audio
means was described by Roush and Hamburger (2). Their
basic control circuit is shown in Figure 3 - 5.

Another motor-driven chronoscope consists of a shallow
drum driven at a constant speed. Inside the drum are three

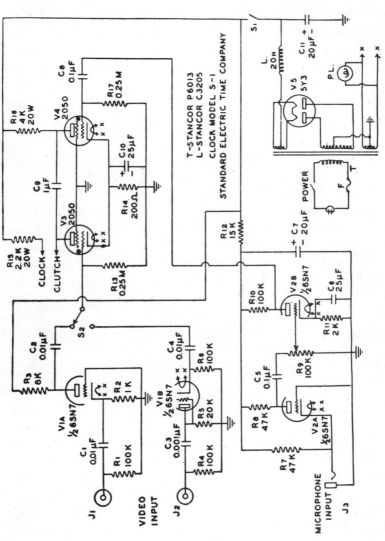

Fig. 3 · 5 —Circuit for video-audio control of an electric stop clock. (From Roush and Hamburger [2], courtesy of the *American journal of psychology*)

spark terminals fixed so that as the signal keys are closed, a spark jumps from the respective terminal through a recording paper to the revolving drum. The recording tape on the revolving drum is scaled with a millimeter rule; thus (knowing the speed of the drum) the time between spark markings can be computed. This apparatus is subject to the error of wanderings of the spark. Photographic registration can be accomplished in this situation by substituting a dot of light and photosensitive paper for the spark and plain recording paper.

MAGNETIC IMPULSE COUNTER-TIMERS

Another timing device is based on the *impulse counter-timer* principle. It is essentially a magnetic vibrator which drives an indicator hand ratchet mechanism. When operated on direct current, the coil attracts a lever when the circuit is made and releases that lever when the circuit is broken externally. The lever strikes a wheel which moves one notch each time the lever strikes it. In this fashion, when DC current is used the instrument operates as a counter, moving an indicator hand attached to the wheel one unit each time the circuit through the counter is made.

When alternating current is passed through the coil, the lever vibrates at a rate equal to the number of half cycles of current. Hence, with 60-cycle current the indicator hand will move 120 units in one second. Since the hand will start as the current begins and stop when the current ends, the number of units moved by the hand is a measure of the interval that the current was on, expressed in units of 1/120 second. An example of this type instrument is shown in Figure 3 - 6. It is convenient to use but has at least two major disadvantages: First, it is very noisy in its operation due to the chatter of the vibrator. Second, it is subject to error due to skipping (10). In the latter instance there is a narrow range of critical voltages at both extremes of which the mechanism will not vibrate at all and within which there are varying degrees of accuracy.

a

b

Fig. 3 - 6- Stoelting impulse counter-timer. (a) Exterior view, (b) interior view, showing ratchet wheel, at top, driven by a spring pawl attached to a pivoted armature actuated by an electromagnet

ELECTRONIC COUNTER-TIMERS

A very precise method of time measurement, similar in principle to the above, is the electronic counter-timer (Fig. 3 - 7). It consists of an accurate source of high-frequency oscillations (crystal-controlled oscillator) and a device to scale or count the number of oscillations made during the period to be

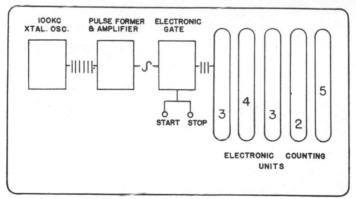

Fig. 3 - 7—An electronic counter-timer, and diagram of how it works. (Courtesy Berkeley Scientific Corp., Richmond, Calif.)

measured (3). The counter consists of electron tube trigger circuits which divide up or scale down the number of oscillations by convenient ratios, such as 2 or 10. These decade or decimal counting units can operate electromagnetic counters (or printing devices) or flash neon indicator lights. The electronic principles on which the scaler units work are discussed in more detail in the following section on counting.

These timer-counters are widely used in industry and are available commercially, but are expensive. Some of them are very versatile, providing a direct reading of time between any two events, a direct reading of the number of events that occur during a precise time interval, a means of measuring low frequencies, precise control of an interval start and stop, and straightforward counting. The timing circuit typically contains the crystal-controlled time base, an electronic gate, start-and-stop input circuits, and five or six decimal counting circuits. The pulses from the start-and-stop circuits open and close the electronic gate to allow the time base frequency to be applied to the cascaded decimal counting units. For an application of the scaler principle to a reaction time device see Holmes and Baker (4).

GALVANOMETER CHRONOSCOPES

Time measurements may be made with a *ballistic galvanometer* (5, 6). An electric current of constant magnitude is caused to flow through the galvanometer coil during the interval to be measured. The coil moves in a direction determined by the direction of the current, through an angle which depends upon the amount of current and the length of time that the current flows. Therefore, with a current of given strength the angle of deflection will depend on the interval during which the current flows. By properly adjusting the current, the angle through which the coil swings can be calibrated to represent time intervals indicated on the galvanometer scale. The principle involved is that of the torsion pendulum.

As this form of chronoscope is commonly used, the galvanometer is connected into a Wheatstone Bridge circuit, the current through which is adjusted by potentiometers. The reaction keys are break keys, one placed in an arm of the bridge and the other placed in series with the galvanometer. At the beginning of the interval, the break key in one of the arms of the bridge is thrown. This cuts out that arm, unbalances the bridge, and sends current through the galvanometer. At the end of the interval, the switch in series with the galvanometer is thrown cutting off the current through the galvanometer.

One advantage of this Wheatstone Bridge arrangement is that, by placing break keys in the opposite arms of the bridge (one to indicate the beginning of one reaction and the other to indicate the beginning of another), it is possible to tell from the direction of the galvanometer deflection which of the reactions occurred first. The amount of deflection indicates the time by which the first preceded the second. Among the disadvantages of this apparatus is the fact that it is necessary to have a known interval on which to check the amount of deflection, since frequent calibration is necessary. Also, the indicator must be read "on the fly," for at the end of the interval the hand returns to zero.

CONDENSER CHRONOSCOPES

A chronoscope which embodies basically these same principles but overcomes the disadvantage of having to be read on the fly is the *condenser type electronic chronoscope* (6, 7, 8). The galvanometer in the Wheatstone Bridge circuit is replaced by a high-quality condenser (Fig. 3 - 8). When the bridge is balanced no charge appears on the plates on the condenser. If the bridge is suddenly unbalanced by breaking the circuit in one of its arms, a charge will immediately begin to flow on to the condenser. The polarity of the charge will depend upon which arm of the bridge was disconnected. When a second key is broken, such that one terminal of the condenser becomes dis-

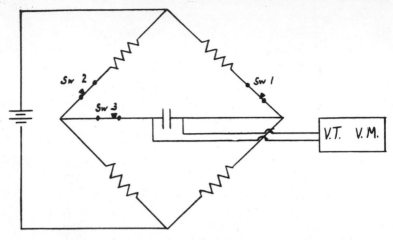

Fig. 3 - 8—Simplified diagram of a condenser chronoscope. The accumulated charge on the condenser is measured by the vacuum-tube voltmeter (V.T.V.M.)

connected entirely from the source of current, the current stops flowing and the charge accumulated on the condenser is trapped. This charge left on the condenser will maintain a constant potential difference across the condenser terminals if the condenser is of sufficiently high quality to prevent leakage.

The amount of charge collected depends upon the time between the opening of the first key and the opening of the second key according to the formula $E_c = E \left(1 - e^{-\frac{t}{RC}}\right)$; where E is the charging voltage, R is the equivalent resistance of the circuit, C is the capacitance of the condenser in farads, and t is the time in seconds. If the charge on the condenser is measured with a vacuum-tube voltmeter, little current will be drawn from the condenser, and the deflection of the meter will remain constant, thus eliminating the need for reading on the fly. After a reading has been made, the condenser may be quickly discharged and prepared for another trial by momentarily closing a switch which shorts the condenser terminals. The chief difficulties with this instrument arise from the need for very high-

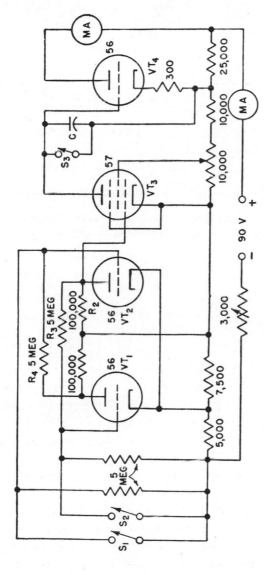

Fig. 3 · 9 —A condenser chronoscope circuit. (By permission from *Handbook of industrial electronic circuits*, by Markus and Zeluff, 1948, McGraw-Hill Book Co., courtesy *Electronics*)

quality parts, particularly the condenser. The range of times which can be measured is a function of the rate of accumulation of charges. Another circuit of this type is shown in Figure 3 - 9.

TIME-DELAY RELAYS

A significant class of timing apparatus has as its elemental function the control of a circuit as a time switch, or time-delay relay. These devices may close a circuit at the beginning of a prescribed interval and open it at the end, or they may open a normally closed circuit at the start and close it again at the end. There are many means for achieving this action, some of which will be discussed later in connection with time markers. Two will be considered here: *thermionic relays* and *electronic time-delay relays*.

A simple regulator of time may be based upon the fact that as electric current passes through a metallic conductor heat is generated and, if the right kind of metal is used, an appreciable expansion occurs. The heat generated and resultant expansion are a function of the amount of current and the time it is flowing. If two metals with different rates of expansion are fused together in the form of a strip, one metal will expand more rapidly than the other causing the strip to bend. By providing the strip with contacts it can be made to close or open a circuit after an appropriate quantity of heat-generating current has passed through it.

Conventional models of thermionic delay relays resemble ordinary relays in appearance except that the auxiliary delay element is placed in series with the coil. A recent model is mounted in a glass envelope on an electron tube plug-in base so that it can be simply mounted (Fig. 3 - 10). Because these units depend on heat for operation, their recovery period is slow. A "cooling off" period is required. This also results in broad accuracy tolerances (20 per cent being common). Where greater accuracy is required, electronic delay devices are superior.

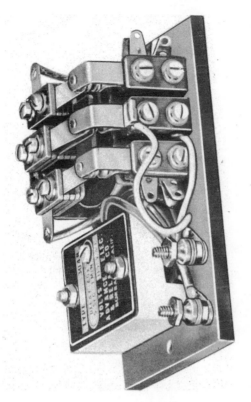

Fig. 3·10—Thermionic time-delay relays. (Courtesy Amperite Co., New York City, and Advance Electric and Relay Co., Burbank, Calif.)

The accumulation of a charge on a condenser provides the most common basis for electronic time-delay function (6, 9). Typically, a condenser is charged through a series resistor until the voltage across it reaches a critical point at which time it discharges through the coil of the relay (or causes a tube to conduct through the relay coil). The time interval may be altered by changing the values of the condenser and the resistor according to the formula mentioned earlier in connection with the condenser chronoscope.

A simplified circuit for such a relay timer is given in Figure 3 - 11. When a switch in the grid circuit (not shown) is closed, charge begins to accumulate on the condenser through

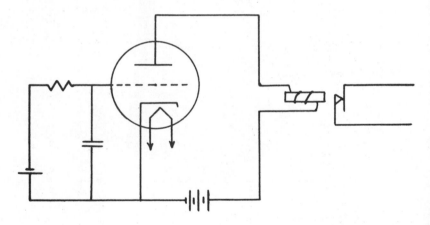

Fig. 3 - 11—Simplified time-delay relay circuit

a series resistor. The tube is connected across the condenser, originally biased so that its grid draws no current. As the condenser charge accumulates, the changing bias alters the plate current until a value is reached which will open the relay, the coil of which is in the plate circuit. If a set of contacts on the relay completes a short circuit across the terminals of the condenser, the condenser will discharge and the circuit will repeat its action at regular intervals.

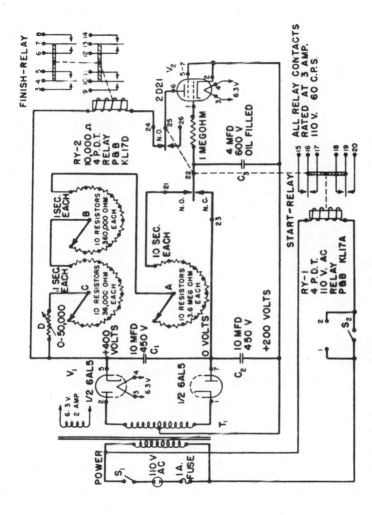

Fig. 3 - 12—Decade interval timer circuit. (From Hunter and Brown [9], courtesy of the authors and the *American journal of psychology*)

Numerous modifications and extensions on this principle permit the use of time-delay circuits to operate time markers, to time test trials, etc. Some models operate with a photoelectric cell replacing the starting switch. Commercial instruments with a wide variety of characteristics are available and are very widely used in laboratory work (see Fig. 3 - 12).

STOP WATCHES

No consideration of timing devices in psychology would be complete without mention of the most frequently employed timepiece, the hand-operated stop watch. It finds its widest applications in timing test trials and in laboratory situations in which accuracy greater than about one-fifth second is not required. Accuracy is dependent chiefly on the skill of the operator, the rate of beat of the watch, and the quality of the lever escapement mechanism. Supplementary devices are available for electrically operating stop watches, and special models are available for widely varied applications. Some are provided with hands for timing two events starting simultaneously but stopping at different times; others have additional dials for cumulative timing.

TIME MARKERS

Time markers make up a major class of timing apparatus. It is their function to provide a graphic record of the passage of time to accompany a record of behavioral events. Such a *time line* is provided on psychological recordings in order that time relations may be read. A time marker may operate directly on a recording medium through a stylus, or it may operate indirectly by opening and closing an electric circuit through a signal magnet or similar recording device. It is most frequently used with kymographs, polygraphs, and chronographs. A chronograph (specialized recorder for receiving a time line), consisting of a drive mechanism for a paper tape on which signal magnets record, was shown in Figures 2 - 4 and 2 -24.

Typically, one of the signal magnets conveys the time line while the others convey stimulus and response characteristics of the experimental situation.

One of the simplest time markers is an ordinary tuning fork with a reed attached to one of the prongs in such a way that vibration of the fork is recorded on a kymograph surface by the scratching of the reed. This marker is started by striking the fork with a hammer or similar piece. The recorded vibrations gradually diminish in amplitude.

An improvement is secured through the use of an electrically maintained tuning fork (Fig. 3 - 13). With such a fork, relatively constant amplitude of the vibratory motion is obtained through the operation of an electromagnetic interrupter device similar to that in the common doorbell. A strong electromagnet is mounted between the prongs of the fork. A small contact plate exists between one of the prongs and the coil of the magnet in such a way that, when the magnet is energized, the prong is pulled toward it. When the prong has moved a certain distance, the contact points separate, and the current to the coil is shut off, the magnetic field collapses, and the elastic tension of the tuning fork returns the prong to its initial po-

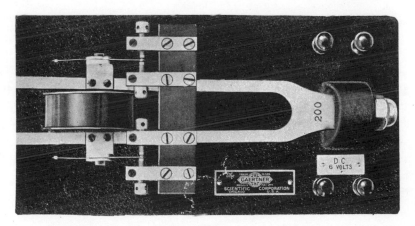

Fig. 3 - 13—An electrically maintained tuning fork. (Courtesy Gaertner Scientific Corp., Chicago)

sition. The contacts are thus again brought together, current flows in the coil of the magnet, and the cycle begins again. The frequency of oscillation is determined jointly by the natural period of the tuning fork and the electromagnetic effects.

This time marker may be used directly on a recording medium by means of a reed attached to the end of a prong, or indirectly by means of its electrical system by placing an appropriate signal marker in series with the interrupter mechanism. When properly adjusted and utilized these forks yield accurate results. However, when the forks are in direct contact with the recording drum, frictional factors mediated by the stylus may distort the period; mechanical damage, par-

Fig. 3 - 14—Marker driven by half-rectified AC. (Courtesy Phipps & Bird, Inc., Richmond, Va.)

ticularly if it affects the position or the elastic qualities of the prongs, may alter the rate of vibration; and improper electrical constants may alter the effectiveness of the magnetic maintaining mechanism. Another variety of electromagnetic marker similar to a tuning fork has its period determined by the rate of oscillation of commercial alternating current. The magnet between the prongs is powered by a half-wave rectifier yielding 60 pulses per second (Fig. 3 - 14).

Pendulum time markers are common. They consist of either a free-swinging or an electrically maintained physical pendulum, which makes contact with a mercury cup at certain points in its oscillation. The seconds pendulum (Fig. 3 - 15) is of this type. Each time the pendulum is perpendicular to the earth, its tip dips into a mercury cup completing an electrical circuit to the signal marker. The conventional metronome is a spring-maintained pendulum with an adjustable period (Fig. 3 - 16). Oscillations of the pendulum are maintained by a spring mechanism which exerts a slight force upon the pendulum each time it reaches one end of its swing. Rate of oscillation is altered by moving the position of the bob on the arm of the physical pendulum. Electrical circuits are controlled by means of contact arms which dip into mercury cups at one or both extremes of the swing.

Similar time markers operate on the principle of a spring bob. The chief difference between a spring bob and the physi-

Fig. 3 - 15—A seconds pendulum (Courtesy Chicago Apparatus Co.)

Fig. 3 - 16—A mercury contact metronome. (Courtesy C. H. Stoelting Co., Chicago)

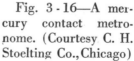

cal pendulum is that the elastic reed or spring is fixed at one end, and the vibration of the reed is influenced by the bob and the elasticity of the spring (Fig. 3 - 17). Such a device may be used to record directly on a kymograph surface by attaching a recording lever to the oscillating element, and the period may be adjusted by changing the distance of the bob from the center of support.

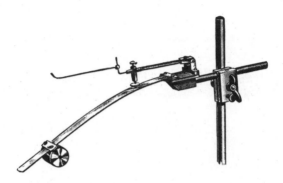

Fig. 3 - 17—A spring bob. (Courtesy C. H. Stoelting Co., Chicago)

Some time markers are based on the principle of a spring-driven clock specially constructed so that each tick or oscillation of the balance wheel is communicated to a lever arrangement which makes a mark on a recording surface. Spring clock markers have for the most part been superseded by synchronous motor clock mechanisms.

Techniques for communicating the time relations from the motor to the recording mechanism differ for various applications. In some instances a contact disk is attached to the motor shaft in such a way that electrical circuits are completed with each revolution or part of a revolution of the disk. In other cases a disk may be supplied with notches into which fit rollers attached to the reeds of microswitches. These rollers usually rest on the edge of the revolving disk, and as they dip in the notches they trip the switches, either opening or closing the circuits through the microswitches. Often oscillations of the motor shaft communicate with some convenient relay circuit. An example of this type, the Phipps and Bird Laboratory Timer, is illustrated in Figure 3 - 18.

It is obvious that synchronous motor devices, in fact most of the time-marking devices mentioned above, are equally suitable for time-control applications—such as timing the length of a test trial or presenting stimuli. The synchronous motor arrangement is particularly useful in this regard because of its adaptability to varied situations. Although synchronous-type motor drives are most widely used, nonsynchronous motors may be used as long as speed of rotation can be controlled accurately. A reliable motor-driven time marker may be made as an attachment for a phonograph turntable. A good quality turntable may be equipped with contact disks and a wiper, it may trip microswitches, or it may operate a mercury switch.

With photographic recording, many of the above time markers can be used to turn a time dot light on and off, or in some other way to register the time on the sensitive surface. One of the most common time markers for use with a photo-kymograph is the rotating sectored disk. This disk is mounted on the shaft of a constant-speed motor and operates as a shutter, interrupting the wash light or intermittently exposing the film to a concentrated light. The result appears as a periodic dark dot or line on the record.

By combining a phonographic recorder and a known source of oscillation, a time line may be produced which has wide application. The lateral disk recording groove cut by a 1000-cycle tone represents an accurate time line conveniently read in milliseconds. The start and conclusion of intervals being measured can be superimposed on this time line by introducing a click or other distinguishable noise pattern into the recorder. The most common applications of such a time line are in calibrating other timers and in time measurement.

Vacuum-tube oscillators find numerous applications as

a

b

Fig. 3 - 18—Motor-operated relay: (a) exterior view;
(b) interior, showing relay and selector switch at top;
notched motor-driven disks, motor, and on-off switch at
bottom. (Courtesy Phipps & Bird, Inc., Richmond, Va.)

time markers. Their frequency can be calibrated readily by a cathode-ray oscillograph, and the rate of oscillation may be varied by altering the appropriate electrical circuit constants. If these oscillations are registered on the recording surface by means of an oscillograph, they provide a dependable time line.

For precise time marking by an electronic oscillator, a square wave is preferred to a sinusoidal pattern. A convenient circuit for squaring sine waves is given in Figure 3 - 19. Where short intervals are needed and the function of the electrical oscillation is to register a time line on a cathode-ray oscillograph, electronic oscillators are very versatile and can be made very

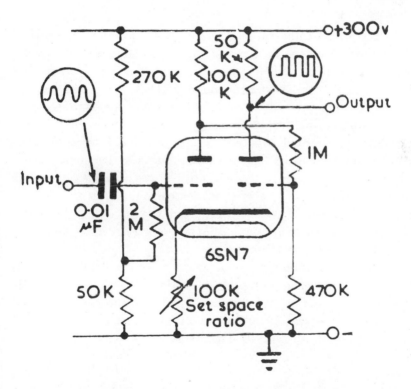

Fig. 3 - 19—Schmitt trigger, for "squaring" of sinusoidal timing wave forms. (By permission from *Electrophysical technique*, by C. J. Dickinson, 1950, Electronic Engineering, London)

accurate. One example, discussed in detail with illustrated circuits by Dickinson (11), consists of a crystal oscillator (operating at 100 kc for convenience) which feeds a number of stages each of which divides the frequency by 10. These lead into a mixer and output stage. One unique property of this arrangement is that two or more frequencies of different amplitudes may be mixed at the output to yield a time line with long and short marks like a ruler. In other words, a 100-cycle pulse of high amplitude might be superimposed over a 1000-cycle pulse of lower amplitude, thus providing a scale with 10 divisions to each hundredth of a second.

CALIBRATION OF TIMERS

The user of any timing device needs to satisfy himself of the reliability of the device and the degree to which its graduations are correct. When a high degree of accuracy is not required, timers are most conveniently checked against one another. A common method of calibrating a time marker is by comparing its time line with that of a tuning fork, both kymographically recorded. Another widely used method is that previously referred to in which a tone of known frequency is recorded phonographically along with a click operated by the timer. This method is accurate and convenient in that it employs equipment typically present in psychological laboratories. Synchronous motor devices of various types have been used extensively as comparison timers.

One calibration device depends upon gravitational force as a speed control and employs a falling object to operate circuit breakers during the course of its fall. The time required for a weight to fall various distances under acceleration of gravity at sea level and 40 degrees latitude is as follows:

Feet *Dropped*	*Time in* *Seconds*
1	0.2533
2	0.3583
3	0.4388
4	0.5067

An example of such a fall-device consists of a round metal ball, released by an electromagnet at the beginning of the test interval, which after falling a given distance hits a light lever normally in contact with a plate, thus breaking the circuit through the contact. Important considerations in the use of such a standard are the possible effects of residual magnetism at the release point and the general efficiency of the circuit breakers.

One of the most useful sources of standardized time intervals for calibration purposes is the rate of oscillation of electrical and electromagnetic waves. For many purposes, commercial 60-cycle house current is the only basis needed. It can be used directly to register a time line with a magnetic oscillograph or on a cathode-ray tube screen; or it can be converted into ratio turns in rotary motion through the use of synchronous motor principles. It may be half-rectified or made to produce uniform pulses which may be integrated on a current-registering meter. Through the use of Lissajou figures, it can be used to measure low frequencies on the cathode-ray oscillograph (see frequency measurement in audition). In some instances, standard broadcast radio frequencies can be used for calibration purposes.

For an interesting discussion of some of the problems encountered in calibrating and comparing time devices, see Dunlap (10).

COUNTING APPARATUS

Mechanical Counters

The simplest forms of counting operations employ mechanical graphic means. A familiar example of a mechanically coupled stylus providing a quantitative record of the number of responses is the finger ergograph. In many cases, the mechanical stylus is supplanted by a signal magnet or oscillograph. A spark graphic record, while not mechanical, is basically similar and may be produced by a mechanically operated switch.

A common type of mechanical counter is the rotary form used in hand calculators and in revolution recorders such as rotary tachometers (speedometers). Several cylinders are notched or geared and arranged in such a way that the revolution of each succeeding cylinder is dependent upon a previous cylinder revolving a prescribed amount. For example, one notched cylinder, driven by a gear or rachet mechanism, may be equipped with a peg every tenth notch. This peg fits in a notch of a second cylinder which also has a peg every tenth notch, and on on. In this manner, a simple decimal accumulator is constructed such that, on the tenth movement of the "units" cylinder, a "tens" cylinder moves once; on every tenth movement of this "tens" cylinder, a "hundreds" cylinder moves once, and so forth.

ELECTROMAGNETIC COUNTERS

In the previous consideration of impulse counter-timers, the on-off characteristics of a direct current were seen to operate an electromagnetic ratchet mechanism which moves an indicator hand one notch each time the circuit through the coil of the electromagnet is closed (Fig. 3 - 6). This is the essential characteristic of electromagnetic counters, some additional examples of which are given in Figure 3 - 20. In each, the activation of a solenoid causes the movement of a lever which in one case operates a drive wheel to which an indicator hand is attached. In the other case the lever turns the notched wheels of a rotary counter similar to that described in the previous paragraph.

Electromagnetic counters are very useful when the counting rate is relatively slow, and when sufficient energy for operating the solenoids is available from the event being counted. Most have critical voltage and current requirements and are subject to error when their normal counting rate is exceeded or their voltage and current requirements are not met. In some instances, clean electrical contacts and appropriate adjustment

Fig. 3 - 20—Mechanical and electromagnetic counters. (Courtesy Veeder-Root, Inc., Hartford, Conn.)

of elastic tension systems and bearings are essential to their successful operation.

ELECTRONIC COUNTERS

When counting at rates exceeding those of electromagnetic counters is desired, an electronic "scaling down" circuit may be used to proportionately reduce the number of impulses. An illustration of such a circuit is given in Figure 3 - 21. Pairs of thyratrons reduce the rate of counting by one-half for each pair, or stage, until a rate is reached which is within the range of the electromagnetic counter.

The manner in which the thyratron tubes operate in this circuit is discussed in most standard textbooks on electronics. In a single pair of thyratrons, the first grid impulse "fires" the first tube, while the firing of the second thyratron extinguishes the first. In this way, each tube responds (fires) to half the number of impulses introduced into the circuit. One of the two thyratrons of the first stage is then coupled to the input of the second stage where a further reduction by a factor of two occurs. When the desired degree of reduction is reached, one of the thyratrons of a stage activates an electromagnetic counter or flashes an indicator light. The same procedure is often accomplished by pairs of triodes instead of gas tubes. For an illustration of a commercial instrument of this type, note Figure 3 - 7; for other circuits see (6).

Another basic form of electronic counter employs electron tubes to convert the impulses to be counted into equal quantities of electricity—usually by transforming them into a square wave of constant amplitude. These quantities are then accumulated or integrated electrically as a charge on a condenser, a displacement of a cathode-ray tube electron beam, or other means. In this manner a vacuum-tube voltmeter may be employed to count the number of times an event occurs.

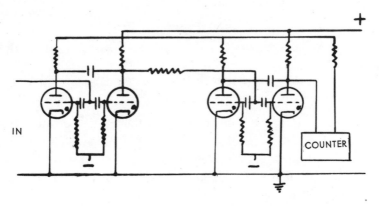

Fig. 3 - 21—A decade counter circuit employing thyratrons

REFERENCES

1. DODGE, R. A. A pendulum-photochronograph, *J. exp. psychol.*, 1926, 9, 155-161.
2. ROUSH, R. G., and HAMBURGER, F. An electronic chronograph for measurement of voice reaction time, *Amer. j. psychol.*, 1947, 60, 624-628.
3. REICH, H. J., and TOOMIN, H. Electronic circuits for the measurement of time and speed, *Rev. sci. instrum.*, 1937, 8, 502-504.
4. HOLMES, J. A., and BAKER, W. The California electronic chronoscope, *Amer. j. psychol.*, 1951, 64, 263-270.

5. KLOPSTEG, P. E. A new chronoscope and fall apparatus, *J. exp. psychol.*, 1917, 2, 253-264.

6. MARKUS, J., and ZELUFF, V. *Handbook of industrial electronic circuits.* New York: McGraw-Hill Book Co., Inc., 1948.

7. JASPER, H. H., and ANDREWS, H. L. A multi-range vacuum tube chronometer, *J. gen. psychol.*, 1936, 14, 248-256.

8. DORCUS, R. M., and HAMBURGER, F. An inexpensive electronic chronoscope, *J. gen. psychol.*, 1938, 18, 439-445.

9. HUNTER, T. A., and BROWN, J. S. A decade-type electronic interval timer, *Amer. j. psychol.*, 1949, 62, 570-575.

10. DUNLAP, K. Chronometric devices in psychological research, *J. gen. psychol.*, 1936, 14-15, 3-30.

11. DICKINSON, C. J. *Electrophysiological technique.* London: Electronics Engineering, 1950.

Chapter 4

Audition

Research in audition, as well as in other fields in which sound is a relevant factor, employs apparatus for the production, control, and analysis of tones. The most significant classes of sound devices are sound generators, amplifiers, and instruments for measuring frequency, intensity, and composition of sounds. The most common tone generator is the audio oscillator. Electronic audio amplifiers permit magnification; and wave analyzers, oscillographs, and voltmeters provide appropriate measurements. Apparatus for the recording and reproduction of sound finds application in nearly every phase of psychological investigation.

BASIC DEFINITIONS AND ACOUSTICAL UNITS

The Nature of Sound

Before consideration is given to specific apparatus for the production, recording, and measurement of sound, it is desirable to turn briefly to concepts and definitions in the field of acoustics. The term *sound* is employed to refer to vibrational energy transmitted in air or other elastic media. The propagation of the energy occurs by means of progressive longitudinal vibratory disturbances in the transmitting medium. The term is also used to designate the sensation produced in the ear by these physical disturbances.

The longitudinal waves which give rise to the sensation of sound are produced by objects in vibration; and a material substance is necessary for their transmission to the auditory sense organ. The most common transmission medium is, of course, air. During transmission the adjacent air particles are slightly displaced—alternately compressed and expanded. In this way the wave front progresses, while the individual air particles remain nearly stationary—merely moving to and fro slightly as the sound disturbance is passing. Sound waves are reflected by appropriate surfaces, and they may be refracted or bent by changes in the medium through which they pass. Sound waves also bend around corners to an extent dependent upon their frequency.

The most common model of a sound wave is that of simple harmonic motion as typified by the movement of a pendulum. The result, with a single frequency of oscillation, is the sine-wave form. Most sound sources give off a compound wave made up of a fundamental frequency, or tone, and a number of harmonics (frequencies in simple multiples of the base frequency). It is the composition of such compound sound waves which determines the complexity of tones. This, in turn, marks the chief differences among various musical instruments, and the differences among spoken vowel sounds in ordinary speech. It is also relevant to studies of the effectiveness of singing.

DIMENSIONS OF SOUND

A major dimension of the physical stimulus of sound is that of *intensity*—the magnitude or strength of the physical stimulus. This magnitude is typically expressed in terms of *sound pressure* or *sound energy*. A psychological dimension closely related to intensity is that of *loudness*, which ranges from soft to loud. It is highly correlated with intensity of the physical stimulus but is also a function of frequency and composition of the sound disturbance. The unit of loudness is the *sone* which corresponds to the loudness of a 1000-cycle tone, 40 decibels above the threshold.

Another major physical dimension of sound is *frequency*, or the number of cycles occuring in a unit of time (usually one second). A *cycle* designates one complete set of values of a pe-

riodic phenomenon, such as one complete sound wave. The reciprocal of the frequency, or the time required for one cycle,
is termed the *period*. The term *double vibration* (dv) is sometimes employed instead of the term cycle. Since it is often desired to express position with reference to the total cycle, the
term *phase* becomes important. Phase is an expression of the
fraction of the total cycle which has elapsed with reference to
some arbitrary point within the cycle and is usually measured
in degrees.

Pitch is a psychological dimension of sound ranging from
high to low. It is most dependent upon frequency, but is also a
function of intensity and composition of the sound wave. Other
psychological dimensions are those of *volume*—in terms of
which sounds are designated from small to large—and *timbre*,
which is a function of the number, the intensity, and the frequency of the overtones making up the sound wave.

THE DECIBEL

The quantification of sound intensity requires a consideration of units of pressure and energy. Instantaneous sound pressure may be expressed in terms of a measurement of the pressure exerted by a sound wave at a given point in time. It is
measured in *bars*, or dynes per square centimeter. The *dyne*
is a unit of force—the force which, when acting upon one gram
for one second, imparts a velocity of one centimeter per second.
Another measure of sound pressure is an average of the instantaneous sound pressures over a complete cycle. The most appropriate average for this measurement is the root mean square
value, also expressed in bars. The symbol "p" is often employed to designate root mean square values of sound pressure.

Sound intensity is also described in terms of the rate of
flow of energy past a fixed plane perpendicular to the direction of propagation. The unit in such a measurement is the erg
per second or the microwatt. The *erg* is a unit of work—the
work done by a force of one dyne acting through a distance of

one centimeter. A *joule* is a work unit equal to 10 million ergs, and a *watt* is a unit of power of one joule per second. The *microwatt*, therefore, equals ten ergs per second.

During the passage of a sound wave through a medium, the intensity, or power radiated through an area of the wave front, is given by the formula:

$$J = \frac{p^2}{r} \text{ ergs per sec per cm}^2;$$

where p is the root mean square sound pressure in bars, and r is the radiation resistance of the medium; r equals the product of the density of the medium and the velocity of sound. For dry air at 20° C. and 760 mm. pressure, r is 41.5; for water it is 143,000.

Under these standard air conditions, the expression for sound energy becomes:

$$J = \frac{p^2}{41.5} \text{ ergs per sec per cm}^2, \text{ or}$$

$$J = \frac{p^2}{415} \text{ microwatts per cm}^2.$$

Average speech power is approximately 100 microwatts. The average voice as loud as possible is about 1000 microwatts; while as weak as possible it is about .1 microwatt; a soft whisper is about .001 microwatt. (It is significant to note that under some conditions the energy is not proportional to the square of the pressure and additional considerations have to be made [2, p. 28].)

The most common expression of sound intensity is one which relates the intensity being measured to a reference intensity. This relationship is expressed as a logarithm of the ratio of the powers of two sounds. The unit is the *bel*, defined as follows:

$$\text{Bel} = \log_{10} \frac{J}{J_0}$$

The *decibel* (db) is equal to one-tenth bel; or ten decibels equal one bel. The number of decibels between a given intensity J and a reference intensity J_0 is given by the expression:

$$N_{db} = 10 \log_{10} \frac{J}{J_0}$$

In actual practice, measurement of intensity may be accomplished through the comparison of two pressures (voltages) in a sound-producing electrical system. Since the intensity is proportional to the square of the sound pressure, the formula for decibels becomes:

$$N_{db} = 20 \log_{10} \frac{p}{p_0} \; ;$$

where N_{db} is the number of decibels above the reference point, p is the given pressure and p_0 is the reference pressure.

Since the use of the decibel presupposes a reference intensity, there might be as many different decibels as there are reference intensities. A common reference intensity in acoustics is taken as 10^{-16} watt per square centimeter. In hearing-loss measurements, the reference is typically the intensity level of the normal limen. Hearing loss is thus measured by the divergence in decibels from the average threshold intensity level at a given frequency and may be expressed by the formula:

$$H.L. = 10 \log_{10} \frac{J}{J_0} \; ;$$

where J is the intensity level of the limen of the person tested and J_0 is the intensity level of the normal threshold.

It is a common misconception that the decibel is a psychological unit. It is a physical unit, although the similarity of the decibel to psychological units is great, since decibels are logarithmic units and in the center intensity ranges closely approximate j.n.d. steps. The decibel is sometimes called a "sensation unit," since it represents a change in power level of a sound equal approximately to the smallest change which the ear can detect. It remains, however, by its nature a physical expression of sound intensity. The term sensation level indicates decibels above the threshold (14).

THE PRODUCTION OF SOUND

HISTORICAL

In the period prior to the electronic wave generator many diverse and ingenious devices for producing tones were used by auditory research workers. Most of these were mechanical in nature employing special techniques for controlling intensity, frequency, and complexity of the tones (Fig. 4 - 1). Of these, the most generally useful today is the *tuning fork,* dependent in its action upon the elasticity of metal. The vibration of the fork is, in effect, a standing transverse wave. The amplitude of sound obtainable from a tuning fork is usually increased by mounting it on a resonance box. A similar device made to have a low rate of oscillation is the *lamella.* It is a modified spring bob, the period of which may be altered by changing the length between the position of the bob and the point of fixation. The lamella found early use in determining the lower limen of pitch. Another familiar instrument for determining upper pitch thresholds is the *Galton whistle,* a miniature whistle with a movable plunger which makes possible a change in pitch.

The use of vibrating bars was common. One of these, the *Koenig bar,* consists of a steel bar suspended by strings. Modern versions of this bar substitute electromagnetic methods of setting the bar in vibration for the old system of striking the bar with a mallet. Another source produces sound by means of vibrating columns of air in pipes, as in organ pipes, flutes, etc., as well as in blowing across the lip of a bottle. Standard sets of pipes, *Quincke's tubes,* are still present in many laboratories and are of historical interest. They consist of glass tubes in a graduated series capable of producing octaves with tones and semitones. The tubes may be used open, or they may be closed by inserting corks. They may be used to demonstrate different tones, beats, and differences in pitch between closed and open pipes.

Other devices include vibrating reeds blown by a bellows arrangement (e.g., *tonometer*), vibrating strings (e.g., *sonom-*

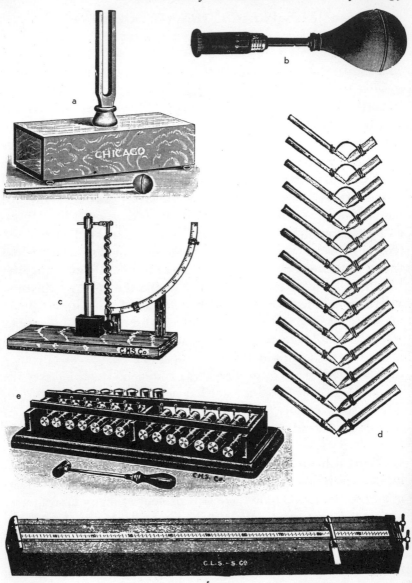

Fig. 4 - 1—Devices for producing tones: (a) tuning fork, (b) Galton whistle, (c) sound pendulum, (d) Quincke's tubes, (e) Koenig cylinders, (f) sonometer. (Courtesy C. H. Stoelting Co., Chicago)

eter), tuned cylinders, and siren disks with air jets. Various methods have been used to control the intensity of sound. One instrument, the *sound pendulum,* consists of a pendulum ending in a hard rubber ball which strikes a block of ebony. Intensity is governed by the angle through which the pendulum falls. Similar devices, termed *acoumeters,* employ metal objects which strike a sounding block after being dropped a known distance. One of the earliest applications of electrical control of intensity of sound in an earphone (Seashore audiometer) employed a modified inductorium with a variable number of turns in the secondary coil—thus achieving linear change of voltage and corresponding change in intensity delivered at the earphones.

Devices similar to most of the above are still widely used. Musical instruments differ from some of them only slightly. Excellent surveys of the operation of these and similar sound sources are available in standard texts of acoustics and the theory of sound. For most laboratory applications, however, in which pure tones need to be produced, the electronic wave generator, or oscillator, is preferred because of its ready control of frequency and intensity.

AUDIO OSCILLATORS

The typical laboratory oscillator is an electrical sine wave generator, the crucial element of which is some form of an oscillating circuit. Important among these are the feedback and the tank circuits. A simple one-tube audio oscillator combining these two circuits is illustrated in Figure 4 - 2.

The basic principle on which one form of feedback oscillator circuit operates is that of mutual induction. Whenever the rate of flow of a current through a magnetic coil changes, the magnetic field about the coil will also change. If the changing lines of force from this coil cut turns of a second coil, a voltage will be induced in the second coil. When the lines of force are expanding with an increase in current through the first coil, the polarity of the induced potential in the second coil will be

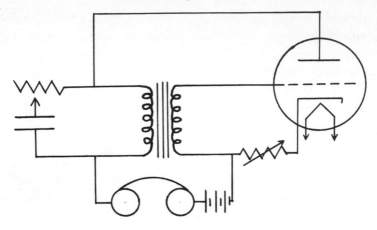

Fig. 4 - 2—A simple audio oscillator

in one direction. As the lines of force contract with a reduction in current in the coil, the induced electromotive force will be opposite in direction.

Assume a simple one-tube vacuum tube circuit in which the primary of an interstage transformer is connected in the plate circuit, and the secondary of the same transformer is connected in the grid circuit. When the filament circuit is turned on, the cathode will begin emitting electrons, and current will begin to flow through the plate circuit. The plate current will be increasing as the cathode heats up, and the current through the primary of the transformer will also be increasing. This increase in current will create expanding lines of force about the primary coil which will induce a potential in the secondary coil, and consequently will produce a change in potential at the grid. If the tube begins at zero bias, and the initial induced bias is positive, the resulting bias will further increase current flow through the tube. This in turn further expands lines of force about the primary coil and induces greater positive bias.

This process will continue until the point is reached at which increase in the positive bias no longer results in increase in plate current—in other words, until the saturation point for the tube is reached. As this limit is approached, lines of force are no longer expanding in the primary coil, and the induced bias becomes lost and returns to zero. Such a loss changes the bias to less positive, which tends to decrease the plate current. This decrease gives rise to contracting lines of force which induce a grid potential opposite in direction, or negative, with respect to the first. The grid, having a more negative value, further decreases the plate current—thus inducing a still greater negative bias. This sequence will continue until the magnetic field about the primary coil has completely collapsed, with the result that a change in grid potential is no longer induced. The grid then returns to its original value and the cycle starts over again. The frequency of oscillation is chiefly a function of the resistance and inductance of the circuit and the characteristics of the tube.

If a parallel resonant (tank) circuit, consisting of a condenser and an induction coil, is connected in series with the plate of a tube, the plate current of the tube may be employed to sustain the natural oscillations of such a circuit. This tank circuit plays an important role in many audio oscillators. When a charged condenser discharges through an inductance which is resonant with it, the discharge is not instantaneous. Instead, oscillations occur in the circuit. The bouncing back and forth of electric charges in such a circuit is termed a flywheel effect because of its similarity to the operation of the flywheel in an ordinary watch. The circuit oscillates because of the energy stored in the magnetic field of the coil and in the condenser. The charge across the plates of the condenser has an effect which may be likened to an elastic medium. The passage of the current through the inductance, on the other hand, sets up an opposing emf which serves to "throw" the charge back to the condenser, where it is "bounced" back to the coil only to be "thrown" back, etc.

Theoretically, if there were no resistance in the circuit, such oscillations would occur indefinitely. Since there is always resistance present, and some of the energy is lost with each oscillation, the activity of the circuit gradually dies out as the charge is dissipated. If, however, some device is employed periodically to charge the condenser and thus restore energy to the circuit, oscillations may be sustained. Control of the rate of oscillation of such a circuit can be achieved by changes in capacitance of the condenser and the value of the inductance and a resistor in the circuit. The presence of the resistor alters the rate of discharge of the condenser.

Some audio oscillators operate on the beat frequency principle. They consist of two high-frequency oscillators interacting

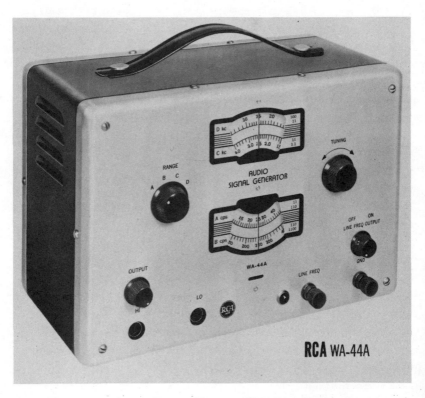

Fig. 4 - 3—An audio oscillator. (Courtesy Radio Corporation of America, Camden, N. J.)

to produce a beat frequency within the auditory range. Ordinarily there is a fixed oscillator and a variable oscillator—both in a high-frequency range. The outputs of the two oscillators are fed into a mixer bridge and into a detector circuit, and the output of the variable oscillator is adjusted to differ by a given amount from the frequency of the fixed oscillator. The resultant interference and summation effects of the two waves as they get alternately in and out of phase gives rise to a third frequency in the detector circuit—the beat frequency. Such wave generators have advantages for close control of frequency and wave composition.

There are many other types of electronic sound generators. An interesting example is an optical tone generator in which an intermittent light of variable frequency is produced by a rotating sectored disk. This light falls on a photocell which converts the optical changes to electrical energy and operates a loud speaker. Forms of oscillating circuits other than those described above are widely used but are beyond the scope of this material, for they are discussed at length in most textbooks on electronics. (See also Hirsh, 2.)

FILTERS

When it is desired to deliver a pure tone, or when for any reason it is necessary to exclude certain frequencies in an electrical or sound wave, filters of either an electrical or an acoustical type are called for. Electrical filters are most commonly employed with tone generators. They operate on the principle of differing reactance of condensers and inductances to varying frequencies. The general function of a filter is to give high resistance to the passage of certain frequencies while giving low resistance to the passage of others. A common form of electrical wave filter, the ladder type employing symmetrical combinations of positive and negative reactances, is shown in Figure 4 - 4. The low-pass filter has as its chief component inductance or choke coils, capitalizing on the increased inductive reactance which such coils have for higher frequencies. The

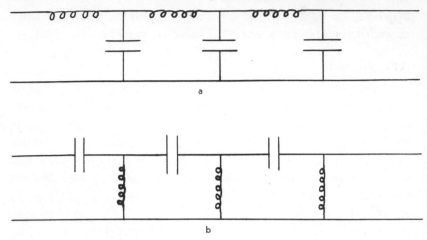

Fig. 4 - 4—Electrical filters: (a) low-pass, (b) high-pass

Fig. 4 - 5—Fixed atten-
uators. (Reproduced
from *The recording and
reproduction of sound*, by
O. Read, published by
Howard W. Sams & Co.,
Inc.)

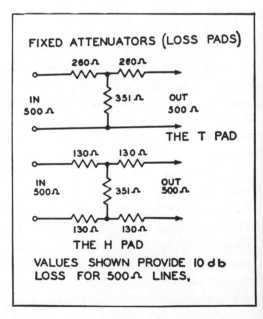

opposite, or high-pass relationship, employs condensers since capacitive reactance reduces as frequency increases.

ATTENUATORS

It is similarly necessary to control the output intensity of electrical tone producers. This is most conveniently accomplished by altering the voltage delivered to the electromechanical device which transforms the electrical waves into sound waves (the *transducer*, in most cases a loudspeaker). To alter this voltage, a network of resistances, termed an *attenuator*, is employed (Fig. 4 - 5). An attenuator is simply a voltage-dividing resistance arrangement. The resistors are arranged in such a way that the voltage is reduced in steps, making calibration in decibel units possible. The output voltage change is accomplished without alteration of important circuit constants, such as output impedance.

SOUND MEASUREMENTS

FREQUENCY MEASUREMENT

The calibration of an oscillator and the analysis of sounds, ranging from those of industrial machines and musical instruments to the human voice, requires techniques for the exact measurement of frequency. The simplest frequency-measuring devices are mechanical in nature. For example, a tuning fork may be made to record its oscillations on a kymograph drum by attaching a reed to the end of the fork. If this record is accompanied by a time line, the number of double vibrations per unit of time may be determined; or some of the other techniques for the recording of tones may be employed, and the resulting record analyzed. Such devices are most frequently employed when a graphic record is desired and an analysis of the wave pattern is to be made.

A simple class of frequency-measuring device is based on the beat principle. In its simplest form two tones, one unknown and the other known, are matched until the known frequency equals the unknown and no beat frequency is heard (or viewed on a device such as a cathode-ray oscillograph). When two simultaneously sounding tones produce a beat, the difference in frequencies between the tones may be determined by counting the number of beats per unit of time.

Lissajou figures.—The cathode-ray oscillograph provides a simple means for measuring frequency. A wave of one frequency is impressed upon one set of plates. (Ordinarily the known frequency is impressed on the horizontal plates.) The second (or unknown) frequency is impressed upon the other set of plates. The pattern on the screen is then a resultant of the two wave forms. If the two frequencies bear some simple numerical relation to one another, a pattern termed a *Lissajou figure* appears on the screen. This figure has a certain number of "humps" in each direction dependent upon the ratio of the frequencies. Examples for simple ratios and phase relationships are given in Figure 4 - 6. It will be noted that the ratio of the frequency on the vertical plates to the frequency impressed on the horizontal is evidenced by the number of humps at the top of the pattern (one for each vertical oscillation) and the number of humps at the side (one for each horizontal oscillation). More complicated patterns may be interpreted in the same way. If the two frequencies are identical, a circle, an elipse, or a straight line appears—depending upon the phase relationship of the two waves.

Stroboscopes.—Another class of frequency-measurement device is based on the principle of stroboscopic motion. A stroboscopic disk of some sort is used. This is either round with alternate white and black segments, in the form of a cylinder ruled with uniform white and black lines parallel to the axis, or a disk or cylinder with evenly spaced black dots. The disk is mounted in such a way that it may be driven at a uniform and controlled speed.

A source of intermittent light, the frequency of which is controlled by the sound for which the frequency is being meas-

RATIO

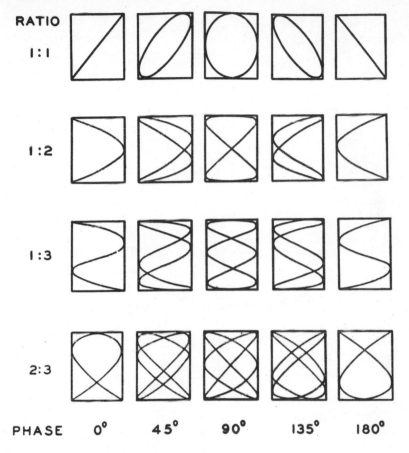

Fig. 4 - 6—Lissajou figures for several frequency ratios. (By permission from *Hearing*, by Stevens and Davis, 1938, John Wiley and Sons, Inc.)

ured, illuminates the disk. One simple method is to have the sound operate a neon bulb (Fig. 4 - 7). When the correct relationship exists between the speed of the disk, the number of segments in the disk, and the rate of oscillation of the light, the image of the stroboscopic disk appears fixed—that is, the dots appear stationary, the sectors do not appear to rotate, etc.

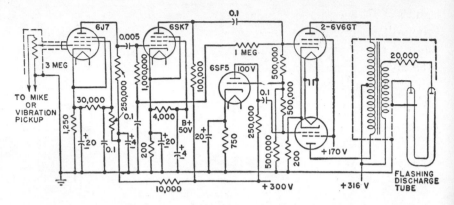

Fig. 4 - 7—Audio-amplifier circuit for stroboscopic frequency measurement. (By permission from *Handbook of industrial electronic circuits*, by Markus and Zeluff, 1948, McGraw-Hill Book Co.; courtesy *Electronics*)

The basic relationship of these three variables when the pattern is standing still is:

$$\text{Speed of rotation in revolutions per second} = \frac{\text{light oscillations in frequency per second}}{\text{number of black segments}}$$

The pattern also stands still for integral multiples or divisions of the frequency given in the formula.

Resonance analyzers.—Commercial devices may be obtained for the direct reading of frequencies (Fig. 4 - 8). Many of these are based on the principle of electrical resonance. It will be recalled that the reactances of a condenser and an inductor vary in an opposite manner with reference to frequency. Because of this reciprocal relationship, a situation may be reached in which a combination of these components will offer no reactance to the passage of a current. This is the phenomenon of resonance, and a circuit is said to be tuned to the particular frequency at which the phenomenon occurs.

It will also be recalled that impedance in ohms is equal to the resultant of metallic resistance and reactance. Similarly, in a simple electrical circuit having a condenser, an inductance, and a resistance in series the current at any moment is equal to the voltage divided by the impedance. When, however, the circuit is tuned to the resonant frequency, reactance is zero, and the only factor limiting current flow in the circuit is resistance. In other words, the current in the circuit will be at a maximum when the circuit is tuned to the resonant frequency.

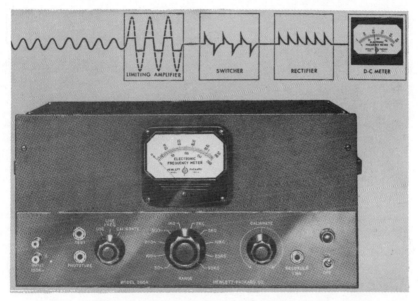

Fig. 4 - 8—A frequency meter with an illustration of its manner of operation. (Courtesy Hewlett-Packard Co., Palo Alto, Calif.)

This principle of resonance is employed in the frequency meter diagrammed in Figure 4 - 9. The unknown frequency is fed into the circuit, as shown, and the variable condenser is adjusted until the circuit becomes resonant as indicated by a maximum reading on the vacuum tube voltmeter. By a simple transformation of the basic reactance equations it can be shown that the frequency of the unknown at this point is given by the equation:

$$f = \frac{1000}{2\pi\sqrt{LC}}$$

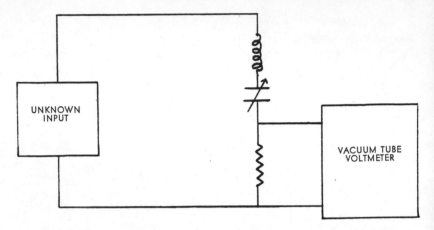

Fig. 4 - 9—Simplified diagram of a resonant frequency meter

where f is in cycles per second, L in henries, and C in micro-farads. Meters may be calibrated so that the frequency can be read directly from the dial of the condenser.

Other methods.—Frequency meters may be based on an integrating or counting principle. Audio frequencies can be converted to a square wave and the square wave used to charge a capacitor (Fig. 4 - 10). This charge, which can be measured on a DC meter, is directly proportional to impressed frequency. The model shown has ranges in multiples of 100 and 300 cps, each extending from zero to its upper limit. The highest range is 30,000 cycles.

Another method for measuring frequency is based upon the principle of the synchronous motor. It will be recalled that the rate of rotation of a synchronous motor is in direct ratio to the frequency of alternation of current driving the motor. (The factor determining the ratio is the number of poles in the motor.) If a source of oscillating current, such as that from a sound system, is used to run a motor of this type (and a system for counting the revolutions of the motor is incorporated), the number of revolutions of the motor in a unit of time will give data from which can be computed the frequency of the driving source.

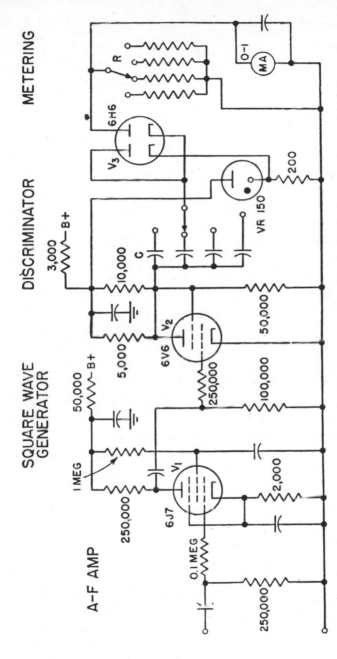

Fig. 4 - 10—Integrating frequency meter. (By permission from *Handbook of industrial electronic circuits*, by Markus and Zeluff, 1948, McGraw-Hill Book Co.; courtesy *Electronics*)

INTENSITY MEASUREMENT

Measurement of sound intensities requires an application of the physical relationships discussed in connection with the decibel unit. One of the most direct methods for measuring sound intensities is by means of the electrical systems producing the sound. The output voltages of an electrical wave generator can be measured accurately and a decibel measurement determined. Such a calculation requires knowledge of the relations between the output of the wave generator and the sound-pressure changes in the transmitting medium (air) produced by the electromechanical transducer (usually a loud speaker). In other words, it is essential that the relationship between the voltages incident upon the transducer and the intensity of the propagated air wave from the transducer be understood. This can be accomplished by a calibration of the transducer (7, 14). Appropriate voltage changes between the generator and the transducer can be brought about by an attenuator.

The measurement of intensity in a given medium, such as in the air of a given room, can be accomplished most simply by means of a *calibrated microphone*. A calibrated microphone is one for which the relationship between the voltage generated and the pressure on the diaphragm has been determined for the particular frequency being measured. By placing such a microphone in a sound field and measuring voltages generated, data are obtained from which the sound pressure at the diaphragm of the microphone can be computed.

Such microphone calibrations can be obtained from manufacturers. Calibration may be accomplished by means of a *Raleigh disk*, based on the principle that a light disk suspended in a sound field will set itself at right angles to the direction of propagation of sound. Each such disk will have a turning moment, or an amount of force necessary to turn the disk. This expression of force can be related to the rate of flow of air past the disk, since it will be proportional to the mean square velocity of the air particles.

Other devices used for calibrating microphones include

thermophones and pistonphones, both of which are instruments for producing known sound pressures. Other less common methods for measuring the intensity of incident sounds are discussed in acoustics texts (14). One.significant method, often used in noise measurement, involves the use of a standard masking noise.

WAVE ANALYSIS

A problem which is very closely allied to the measurement of frequency is that of breaking up a complex wave pattern into its components. Particularly in the study of musical sounds is the investigator interested in such analysis, for the quality of a musical tone is determined by the relative amplitudes and frequencies of its overtones. It often becomes desirable to determine both the frequencies and the amplitudes of the components of a complex wave pattern.

Electric analyzers.—The simplest way of doing this is by means of a commercial wave analyzer. Such a device resembles the resonance frequency meter mentioned previously. The variable condenser may be adjusted successively to the points of resonance for the fundamental component and the harmonic frequencies of a complex wave. In this way the frequencies of the components can be determined, and the amplitude of the tone to which the meter is tuned will be indicated by the voltage drop across the resistor. The circuit constants in this situation are arranged such that the impedance to frequencies to which the circuit is not tuned will be very high. This prevents the amplitude of a harmonic from being influenced by the amplitude of its fundamental tone or other harmonics.

The heterodyne principle employed in radio receivers may also be used in detecting component frequencies of a complex wave. The complex wave and the output of an audio oscillator are placed in the same series circuit so that a beat frequency may be produced. This circuit is then fed into a detector and an amplifier. The beat frequency may be singled out and amplified a known amount. By slowly progressing through the range of the audio oscillator, the fundamental and the harmonic frequencies may be determined by the evidence of the beat wave on some form of output indicator. The detector-amplifier system may be set to register (or to pass) a beat wave of only a certain low frequency. Thus the presence of energy from a beat wave in an output meter will indicate the presence of a component, and by appropriate calibration of the oscillator output and the amplifier gain the relative amplitudes of the components may be indicated on the output meter.

Graphic and mathematical analysis.—It is possible to analyze a complex wave from an oscillographic representation of that wave, such as might be obtained from a photograph of the screen of a cathode-ray oscillograph. A mathematical expression for the complex wave form may be given. According to the mathematical expression known as Fourier's series, a complex periodic wave may be broken down into component simple harmonic motions. In Fourier's equation expression is made of complex wave forms as a sum of component wave forms whose frequencies are multiples of the fundamental frequency. For a simple discussion of this method see Lemon and Ference (9).

Such an analysis may be accomplished graphically, by a procedure which is briefly as follows. Beginning with the graphical representation of the complex wave, the linear distance of one cycle of the fundamental frequency (abscissa : time) is divided into segments corresponding to the order of the harmonics being analyzed. Ordinates to the curve are then drawn at the division points, and the algebraic sum of these ordinates within the cycle is obtained. The ordinate value at any point on the curve represents the amplitude due to that particular harmonic and the amplitude at the given point due to other harmonics. By a series of comparisons of the ordinate values, the amplitude of each harmonic may be obtained. Equations are available (10, 3) for the determination of these values and that of the fundamental. This procedure for fairly complex waves becomes laborious.

AUDIOMETRY

It is often desirable to have a clinical measure of the ability of an individual to hear sounds. This requires apparatus for producing tones of certain frequency, regulating their intensity, and delivering them through the air or through the bones of the head (2, 11). The apparatus for this purpose is termed an *audiometer* (Fig. 4 - 11). In its most common form the audiometer consists of a vacuum tube oscillator equipped to produce tones of several fixed frequencies (or a variable frequency) at calibrated levels of intensity. To this is added an earphone for delivering the tone to the subject's ear, or a vibrator device for transmitting sound oscillations to the skull for conduction to the inner ear. If fixed frequencies are employed, they usually consist of standard octave values within the range of at least as low as 128 cycles per second and as high as 8192 cycles per second. Many go beyond these limits and provide smaller frequency intervals than octaves.

Control of intensity is achieved by means of a built-in attenuator system. Intensity calibration is made about a normal threshold value for each frequency according to American Standards Association specifications, see Hirsh (2, p. 321-327). The standard unit is the decibel, and control is possible in intervals of five decibels or less. Measurement is accomplished by a psychophysical method (most commonly some modification of the method of limits employing ascending and descending series). The limen as measured is the expression in decibels of the departure of the individual's threshold from the average threshold intensity level for the particular frequency being measured.

The standard graphical presentation of the data received from such an audiometer is termed an *audiogram* (Fig. 4 - 12). This graph contains a zero hearing loss line which represents the average threshold intensity. Decibel levels with reference to that intensity are given on a vertical axis for specific frequency points on a horizontal axis. The individual thresholds

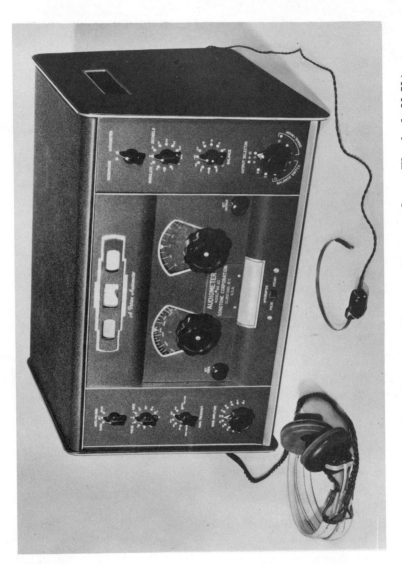

Fig. 4·11—An audiometer. (Courtesy Sonotone Corp., Elmsford, N.Y.)

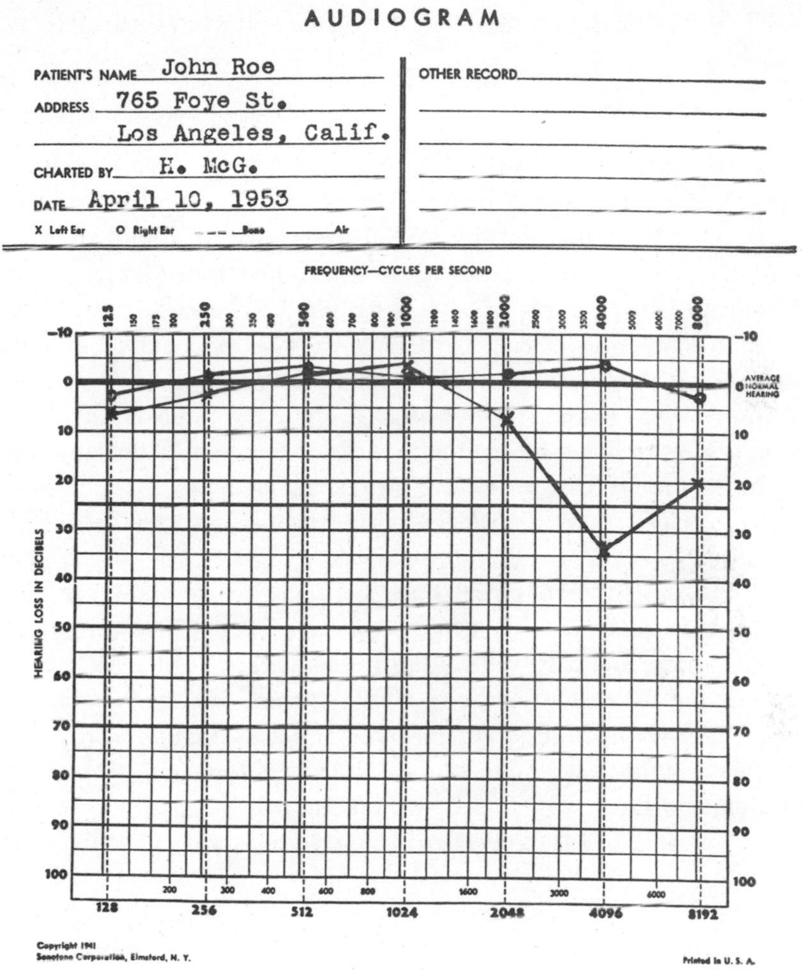

AUDIOGRAM

PATIENT'S NAME __John Roe__   OTHER RECORD_____

ADDRESS __765 Foye St.__

__Los Angeles, Calif.__

CHARTED BY __H. McG.__

DATE __April 10, 1953__

X Left Ear   O Right Ear   ___ Bone   _____ Air

Fig. 4-12—An audiogram for a person having high tone deafness in one ear

for each ear at each frequency may be plotted and these points
joined by straight lines to give a continuous graph of hearing
loss as a function of frequency. A drop in the graph for one
ear at the high end of the scale indicates a high-frequency loss,
breaks in the curve may indicate tonal lacunae, and so forth.

THE RECORDING AND REPRODUCTION OF SOUND

Disk Recording

The general procedure involved in lateral disk recording is as follows. The sound to be recorded is picked up by a microphone and led into an audio amplifier where it is amplified to a point where sufficient power is developed to activate an oscillograph in the form of a cutting head. The cutter engraves a modulated groove in a revolving disk made of special material. The modulations in the groove correspond to the form of the original sound waves incident upon the microphone. The sound is reproduced by having a pickup device ride the grooves of the record, transforming the lateral movements of the needle into electrical waves which are again amplified and delivered as sound waves from a loud speaker (4, 12).

The major parts of a disk recording instrument are the microphone, amplifier, cutting head with its cutting stylus, recording disk, and a turntable equipped with a feed mechanism for moving the cutter across the disk as the disk revolves under the cutter. For reproduction the conventional phonograph pickup head, amplifier, and loudspeaker are required. Of these components those which are unique to this recording process are the cutting head, the recording medium, and the feed mechanism.

Recording heads.—Since the recording head is a device for transforming electrical oscillations into movements of a stylus, it falls into the general class of electrically driven oscillographs (Fig. 4 - 13). The principles upon which commercial cutters operate are those mentioned earlier in connection with general recording instruments. The two most generally used are (1) magnetic cutters which consist of an armature with attached cutting stylus suspended in an electromagnetic field in such a way that changes in the magnetic field cause lateral vibrations of the armature and stylus, and (2) crystal cutters in which the lateral vibration of the cutting stylus results from the bending of a long crystal when a potential difference is applied across its two sides. The chief differences between a good and poor recording head lie in the frequency response of the oscillograph and its ability to record high volumes without distortion.

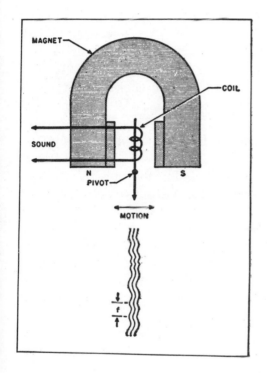

Fig. 4 - 13—A simplified diagram of a lateral disk recording head. (Reproduced from *The recording and reproduction of sound,* by O. Read, published by Howard W. Sams & Co., Inc.)

Styli.—The cutting of the groove is accomplished by a replaceable stylus which fits into a small chuck in the recording head proper. It may be likened in function to a metal lathe tool, for it cuts into the recording disk (Fig. 4 - 14). It resembles such a tool somewhat in shape, having a flat cutting face with sharp, highly polished edges and a microscopically rounded point. Only a small portion of the stylus, the tip, does the cutting. The sharpness and smoothness of the tip and face edges play a major role in determining the amount of surface noise recorded. For this reason the life of all styli is limited, and considerable care in the choice of a stylus is necessary. The angle which the face of the stylus makes with the recording material is termed the *cutting angle* and is a critical factor in high-quality recording.

The life of a stylus and the quality of reprduction depend upon the material of which the stylus is made. The cheapest styli are made of steel. These dull quickly due to frictional heat, cannot be resharpened, and have an inferior frequency response characteristic. They do not chip and they satisfactorily record speech and medium tones, which makes them desirable for use with inexperienced operators. The most efficient styli for quality recording have sapphire points, which are very hard and will take a high polish. Because of this hardness they are brittle and subject to chipping, if dropped. Their life is much longer than that of steel styli, and, if they are not chipped, they may be resharpened many times. Various styli of metal alloys with efficiency between these two extremes are also manufactured. Of these, the most common is termed a stellite stylus

Fig. 4 - 14 — Stylus angle adjustment. (Reproduced from *The recording and reproduction of sound*, by O. Read, published by Howard W. Sams & Co., Inc.)

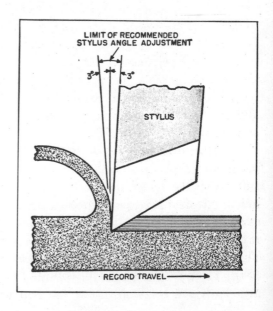

after the alloy of which its tip is made. It is harder than steel but softer than sapphire; it does not chip and may be resharpened.

Disks.—The materials used for laboratory recording are those manufactured for *instantaneous* recording. The records are to be used for immediate playback and are not ordinarily made as masters for the production of the pressed type records —the familiar phonograph records. The difference between pressed and instantaneous records is important because of the necessary difference in their handling at playback. The ordinary commercial record is stamped in a material to which an abrasive has been added to reduce groove wear due to faulty needle points. The needle wears into the groove, rather than the groove wearing to fit the needle. The reverse is true in instantaneous recordings. Because such an abrasive is not used, the groove will be ruined quickly by use of improper needles. Special reproduction needles in good condition are necessary to preserve the materials in instantaneous recording.

The typical instantaneous recording disk consists of an aluminum or paper backing on which there is a heavy coating of lacquer, the chief ingredient of which is cellulose nitrate. Lesser-used materials include metal, such as aluminum, and wax when duplicates are going to be "processed." Because of the popularity of home recorders, these record blanks are readily available in a variety of qualities and sizes (6½, 8, 10, 12, and 16 inch). Three common makes are the Audiodisc, Presto, and Recordisc.

Drive and feed mechanism.—Most recording apparatus permits cutting the record from the inside out or from the outside in on the recording disk. Since there is no groove to follow as in playback, a mechanical arrangement is necessary for carrying the cutting head across the disk at an appropriate rate. There are three main types of such feed mechanisms. The most common, because of its economy, is the fan-gear drive (Fig. 4 - 15). The cutter is mounted on a pivoted arm. This arm is driven in an arc by a fan and worm gear on the main drive shaft. The chief objection to this form of drive is that the cutter changes its angle with reference to the cut as it traverses the record. A superior mechanism employs a lead screw mounted either above or below the turntable. The cutter rides on a carriage which travels along the lead screw as it turns (Fig. 4 - 15). The lead screw is driven by the turntable drive mechanism. A third feed mechanism employs such a lead screw but has it mounted beneath the carriage and turntable.

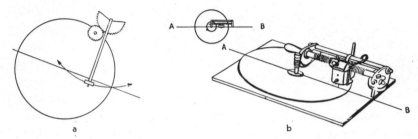

Fig. 4 - 15—Drive mechanisms: (a) fan gear, (b) lead screw. (By permission from *How to make good recordings*, 1948, published by Audio Devices, Inc., New York)

Typical commercial disk recording apparatus may consist of separate turntable and amplifier, or both features may be combined in one instrument. Many turntables are equipped for reproduction as well as recording, and many new models include two recording heads—the second one being for microgroove recording. Some instruments are specialized for re-recording or *dubbing*. Dubbing refers to the process of copying a record by recording it. This may be accomplished by leading directly from a pickup arm on one turntable (on which the record is being played) to the amplifier of a recorder which cuts a new record on a separate turntable. This process is used very widely in laboratory work, for it is often desired to extract portions of a recording for later use, or to prepare recorded auditory stimulus series in such a way that any stimulus may be reproduced at will.

MAGNETIC RECORDING

General procedures and theory.—Magnetic recording is made possible by the fact that a magnetic material may be magnetized in small sections with various strengths of magnetic fields. In this way magnetic patterns which correspond to specific wave forms may be produced in such materials. By application of principles of induction, these varying magnetic fields may be made to produce electrical wave forms. In magnetic recorders the magnetic material (wire, tape, disk, or film) is drawn past a recording head or device for magnetizing the material. The amount of magnetization at any instant is determined by an electric signal impressed upon the recording head through its electromagnetic coil. As the wire or tape passes through the recording head it becomes variously magnetized and remains so. The variation in the magnetization corresponds, within limits, to changes in the electrical signal impressed on the recording head.

To play back such a recording the magnetized material is drawn past a playback or pickup head. The variations in the magnetic field about the wire or tape induce corresponding voltage changes in a coil in the pickup device. For editing and re-use purposes small portions (or all) of the recorded pattern in the magnetic material may be "erased." This is accomplished by an erase head for impressing a uniform field on the material, thus replacing the old fields and making the material ready for re-use. In practice, the three functions above —recording, playback, and erasing—may be accomplished through a single head. A block diagram of a wire recorder is shown in Figure 4 - 16.

Certain features of magnetic recorders are of more interest to the laboratory worker than others. Among those of major interest are: magnetic materials used, drive mechanisms, heads, problems of speed, fidelity, and equalization, and specialized applications and modifications. The following material considers some of these problems in more detail.

Magnetic media.—The most common magnetic materials for recording purposes are fine metal wire about .004 inch in diameter, thin plastic or paper tapes to which a coating of magnetic material has been added, and paper or composition disks and moving films similarly coated. Major considerations in the evaluation of a medium include frequency response characteristics (fidelity), noise level, signal amplitude, and running speed.

For the human voice with low-frequency response (up to 3000 or 4000 cps) a carbon or chrome steel wire of low coercive force is adequate. For higher frequencies in wire, special stainless steels of high coercive force are needed. Some plated brass wires will yield high-frequency response. Tapes, in general, capitalize on their insulating properties and the resulting smaller self-demagnetization. Greater fidelity of high frequencies may be produced with them, and there is less "cross talk." A reasonably flat response to 9000 or 10,000 cps may be obtained with appropriate materials and recording circuits.

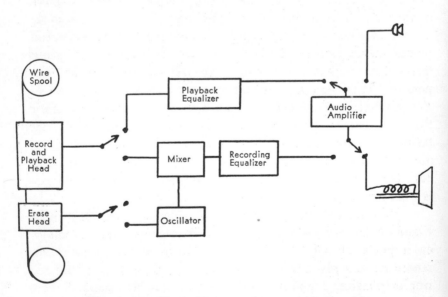

Fig. 4 - 16—Block diagram of a magnetic recorder

The speed at which the material is driven has practical implications. A slow drive ordinarily permits a longer record to be made without changing the medium. On the other hand, frequency response is closely related to the speed of drive. In general, the greater the speed the greater the fidelity of reproduction. This, of course, soon reaches practical limits. Wire speeds are standardized at 24 inches per second. Tapes, because a greater cross-sectional area is exposed to the head, are run at much slower speeds. The most common speed is 7.5 inches per second. Tapes also present practical editing advantages, for sections of the tape may be cut out and the ends joined with glue or scotch tape.

Heads.—A major part of any magnetic recording device is the magnetic head for recording and playback. As the magnetic material is pulled through the head, it becomes magnetized by the field produced by the head; as it is pulled back through the head for playback purposes, it induces voltage changes in the head coil. Typical record-reproduce heads, for both wire and tape recorders, consist of a coil, pole pieces, and a gap through which the material passes and in which the magnetization takes place. The head may be either open or closed in the sense that the wire or tape may have to be threaded through the pole pieces (closed type) or the wire or tape may pass through a groove in the pole pieces (open type).

The recording is accomplished while the material is in the gap between the pole pieces. The material may be longitudinally magnetized or, in the case of tape, may be perpendicularly magnetized. Because most of the magnetization occurs between the pole pieces, the width of the recording gap is a major determiner of the frequency response.

Equalizers.—The function of the equalization circuits in Figure 4-16 is to compensate for nonlinearity in the frequency response characteristics of the recording material and the recording and playback head. In general, the recording equalizer emphasizes high frequencies, and the playback equalizer boosts low frequencies. The combined result is a reasonably flat over-all response curve on reproduction. Closely related to this problem of frequency discrimination is the need for achieving in the amplifiers and associated circuits a large ratio between signal level and noise level. Chief factors, other than frequency effects and amplifier noise, contributing to a high noise level are the magnetic properties of the material, magnetic transfer or cross talk, mechanical effects, and stray static fields.

Drive mechanism.—The mechanism for driving the material past the heads is an important consideration in the evaluation of a magnetic recorder. If the drive speed varies from moment to moment, the result is a perceptible "wow" in the recorded result. Such speed variation may result from imperfections in gear teeth, irregularities in belts and pulleys, flat spots and slippages in drive rollers, etc. The amount of wow which may be tolerated depends upon the use for which the recording is made—the spoken word, for example, is less influenced than musical sounds.

To minimize wire and tape breakage it is essential that the material remain under a relatively constant tension. This is particularly important with reference to driving and braking systems when the direction of the material is reversed.

The general forms of drive mechanisms in use include spool drives, which employ rubber-surfaced friction-drive rollers, belt and pulley arrangements, and capstan drives in which the magnetic medium is wrapped around a revolving wheel and is thus driven by friction at a constant speed. Special drive mechanism features are incorporated in all commercial recorders designed for specific purposes. For example, an office dictation recorder usually incorporates special stop and automatic throwback features to facilitate transcription.

OPTICAL RECORDING ON FILM

For routine laboratory purposes, the recording of sound on film by photographic methods similar to those used in cinema reproduction has been limited. The chief reason for this lies in the relative difficulty of the processing technique. The procedures are interesting, however, because of the principles which make the technique specially applicable to situations requiring a combination of photographic images and sound recording on the same medium.

The basic methods for optical recording on film are those involving *variable film densities* and *variable film areas* (Fig. 4 - 17). The ultimate goal of both is to transfer changes in sound energy into changes on the photographic film, which for reproduction may be reconverted to sound changes. In variable density recording the sound wave to be recorded is used

Fig. 4 - 17 — Optical sound recording: (a) variable density, (b) variable area. (Reproduced from *The recording and reproduction of sound*, by O. Read, published by Howard W. Sams & Co., Inc.)

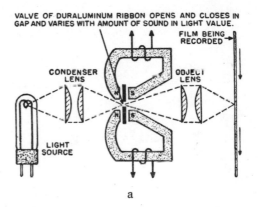

VALVE OF DURALUMINUM RIBBON OPENS AND CLOSES IN GAP AND VARIES WITH AMOUNT OF SOUND IN LIGHT VALUE.

FILM BEING RECORDED

CONDENSER LENS

OBJECT LENS

LIGHT SOURCE

a

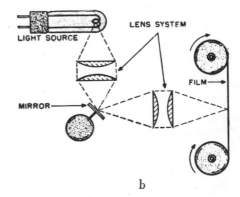

LIGHT SOURCE

LENS SYSTEM

FILM

MIRROR

b

to modulate an aperture or light valve in an optical system focussed in a fine line across a band of film. The light valve is like an optical oscillograph in the sense that it will open and close with each oscillation in current through it; how far it will open each time will depend upon the intensity of the sound. In this way, frequency is recorded as the number of changes in film density (on-off) per unit of time, while intensity is recorded by relative darkness (density) of these changes. For playback, a focussed light source passing through the film falls upon a photoelectric cell (Fig. 4 - 18). The density changes in the film modulate the light falling on the photocell, and the output of the phototube is amplified and fed into a loudspeaker.

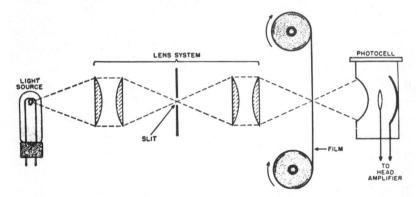

Fig. 4 - 18—Basic system for reproducing sound on film. (Reproduced from *The recording and reproduction of sound,* by O. Read, published by Howard W. Sams & Co., Inc.)

Variable area recording converts frequency and intensity changes into variations in the relative exposed and unexposed portions of a narrow band of film. This is also accomplished by means of an oscillographic operation. A reflecting or shadow-casting oscillograph is made to respond to frequency and intensity changes in the incident sound. In this way a shadow of fixed density but of variable area is produced on the film. The pickup method is essentially the same as with variable density records. Modulations in light upon the cell are now dependent upon the number of changes in exposed film area per unit of time (frequency) and the relative amount of the area which is exposed or shaded (intensity). A modification of variable area recording (termed push-pull recording) is currently the most common form of optical cinema recording.

SOUND ROOMS

Laboratory work in any sense field requires, on many occasions, that the sense being investigated be isolated from undesirable or extraneous sources of stimulation. Light-proofing a room for visual studies is accomplished with little expense and relative ease by appropriate blinds and light traps. Isolating a portion of the laboratory from extraneous sounds, on the other hand, is a much more difficult problem. Ordinary walls transmit a great deal of noise, as do the usual foundation, floor, and ceiling. An identical sound source will not appear the same to the ear in one room as it does in another, because of the different absorption and reverberation characteristics of the rooms. For these reasons, it is ordinarily necessary to set aside an area of the laboratory for sound work and to have a special acoustically designed room installed. As such, the "soundproof room" becomes a permanent and widely used portion of any laboratory.

There are two main problems involved in the design of the sound laboratory. One is the insulation of the room from extraneous sounds—the problem of soundproofing. The other is the appropriate treatment of the interior of the room to control the absorption and reflection of sound waves originating within the room.

SOUND INSULATION

Undesired sounds may be transmitted to a laboratory room by several means. In the first place, they may be transmitted through openings and through partitions or walls. Common openings are cracks around doors and windows, hot-air heating systems, and ventilating ducts. Passage of sound through a partition may be likened to that of light through a solid medium—portions of an incident wave are reflected and absorbed, the rest is transmitted. A significant amount of sound in classroom buildings is transmitted by the solid structural members of the building. Street noises are picked up by the foundation and carried throughout the building. The din of student movement is similarly passed through the framework of the building, as are motor and other equipment noises. Most often these structural vibrations are transmitted to surfaces like walls or furniture which act as sounding boards. The soundproofing of a room reduces the contribution of all of these sources.

A certain number of openings to any room are necessary for entrance, ventilation, and transmission of electrical power. Entrance is ordinarily accomplished by a set of double or triple doors made of low conduction material, carefully fitted and padded, and separated by an air space. In a "floating room" the floor and walls between the doors are constructed so as to present a discontinuous sound path. Ventilation, electric power, and outside leads to equipment are most often accomplished by ducts. Ducts specially constructed for the purpose are capable of greatly attenuating the sound passing through them. Major relationships here are those between sound transmission and the length, diameter, and absorption characteristics of the tubes and their lining.

The most common means for reducing vibrations transmitted through structural members of a building is to use a "floating room," or a room within a room. This procedure introduces a discontinuity in the solid conductors, thus greatly attenuating vibrations from this source. Contact between the inner and outer rooms is made by means of flexible and elastic supports, and isolators with high damping qualities. Specially constructed ceiling and wall "isolators" and floor "chairs" are available. Common padding material in these supports are cork, felt, and rubber. Floor suspension systems include springs and elastic steel cradles. Layers of dry sand and cork have been used in isolating an inner concrete floor from the outer structure. Aside from necessary isolators and supports, the inner walls and ceiling are separated from those of the outside building by air space and layers of sound absorbent material. Recent developments have put on the market special acoustical "blocks" for use in wall structure where a minimum of transmission is desired.

The degree to which insulation of a room is achieved is indicated by means of sound intensity measurements. The minimum noise level, expressed in decibels, which may be tolerated varies with the purpose for which the room is to be used. One quantity used in the evaluation of specific acoustical insulating material is *transmission loss* which indicates, in decibels, the amount that sound energy is reduced in transmission through a unit of the material. Convenient tables which give this information for many materials are available in texts on architectural acoustics (13, 14); most recent developments are published in the *Journal of the acoustical society of America*. Another useful quantity is the *absorption coefficient* of the material; this indicates the fraction of incident sound which is absorbed by the material. Values of this quantity for commercial materials are also available. A related measure which takes into account the frequency of incident sounds, is the *acoustic impedance* of the material.

SOUND CHARACTERISTICS OF ROOMS

The sound which is heard by a subject is the product of factors other than the sound source. Important among these are the amount of reverberation of sound in the room, dead spots or positions of sound focus, echoes, and resonance effects. Reverberation is the term used to describe the persistance of sound after the source stops. It is a result of successive reflection and absorption of the sound by the air and objects or boundaries of the room. The absence of such reverberation is usually the first thing which is noticed upon entering a "dead" or highly absorbent room. The chief factor determining the amount and length of reverberation is the absorbing qualities of the surfaces of the room. The typical soundproof room is constructed "dead" or highly absorbent. Temporary measures can then be taken to increase the amount of diffusion and reverberation for specific purposes—by introducing reflecting surfaces and irregularities in the contours of the room.

A room which is highly absorbent will, of course, make customary sounds appear unnatural. This is particularly evident in binaural effects. Ordinarily, stimuli are received by both ears, part directly, the rest by reflection. The absence of reflected components is readily noticeable; the voice is made to sound shorter and more lifeless. Too much reflection causes spoken words to run together, making it difficult to understand speech. Selective absorption or reflection may at times be a problem. This is due to the fact that most materials, including air, absorb some frequencies more readily than others.

REFERENCES

1. STEVENS, S. S., and DAVIS, H. *Hearing*. New York: John Wiley & Sons, Inc., 1938.
2. HIRSH, I. J. *The measurement of hearing*. New York: McGraw-Hill Book Co., 1952.
3. OLSON, H. F., and MASSA, F. *Applied acoustics*. Philadelphia: Blakiston's Son & Co., 1934.
4. READ, O. *The recording and reproduction of sound*. Indianapolis: Howard W. Sams & Co., 1949.
5. BORING, E. G. *Sensation and perception in the history of experimental psychology*. New York: D. Appleton-Century, Inc., 1942.
6. MARKUS, J., and ZELUFF, V. *Handbook of industrial electronic circuits*. New York: McGraw-Hill Book Co., 1948.
7. MASON, W. P. *Electromechanical transducers and wave filters*. New York: D. Van Nostrand Co., 1942.
8. MASSA, F. Loudspeaker measurements, *Electronics* (1936), IX, no. 2, 18f.
9. LEMON, H. B., and FERENCE, M. *Analytic experimental physics*. Chicago: University of Chicago Press, 1946.

10. COLE, L. S. Graphical analysis of complex waves, *Electronics* (1945), XVIII, no. 10, 142 - 145.

11. BUNCH, C. C. *Clinical audiometry.* St. Louis: C. V. Mosby, 1943.

12. FRAYNE, J. G., and WOLFE, H. *Elements of sound recording.* New York: John Wiley & Sons, Inc., 1949.

13. KNUDSEN, V. O., and HARRIS, C. M. *Architectural acoustics.* New York: John Wiley & Sons, Inc., 1950.

14. BERANEK, L. *Acoustic measurements.* New York: John Wiley & Sons, Inc., 1949.

CHAPTER 5

Vision

Instrumentation in visual research centers around the manipulation and control of the physical stimulus; for accurate measurement and control of intensity, wave length, and composition of the visual stimulus is essential in the study of psychological attributes of perceived brilliance, hue, and saturation. In some instances, visual images must be produced and systematically varied; and several classes of visual apparatus have been developed in connection with specific problems, such as the measurement of visual acuity, color sensitivity, and perceptual abilities. Before these problems and apparatus are considered, a short review of basic concepts from the field of optics may be helpful.

SOME BASIC CONCEPTS

THE NATURE OF LIGHT AND COLOR

For laboratory purposes, light may be described as the visible portion of the electromagnetic spectrum, which extends from slow oscillations of long wave length, through radio waves, X-rays, and gamma rays, to cosmic rays of very high frequencies and small wave lengths (Fig. 5 - 1). Light is thus conceived as a wave motion, an electromagnetic radiation with wave lengths very much shorter than radio waves and much longer than X-rays. The visible spectrum (Fig. 5 - 1) is most commonly designated in wave lengths (rather than frequency), and extends from about 400 millimicrons[1] wave length (violet) to

---

[1] A millimicron is equal to 10^{-6} millimeter. Another unit in terms of which these wave lengths are often expressed is the angstrom. The angstrom is one-tenth of a millimicron, or 10^{-7} millimeter.

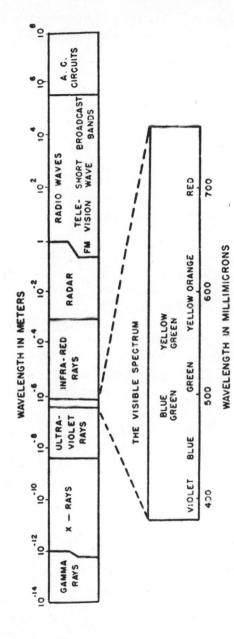

Fig. 5-1—The electromagnetic (radiant energy) and visible spectra. (From Chapanis [6] courtesy of the author and publishers)

about 700 millimicrons (red). It is bordered on one side by the invisible ultraviolets and on the other extreme by the invisible infrareds.

Within these limits fall the stimuli for color experiences of the eye. When a light incident upon the eye is pure, or is made up of waves of a single frequency or wave length, the light is said to be *monochromatic*. When a light wave is complex in the sense of being made up of more than one wave length, it is termed *heterochromatic*. The light given off by most natural and laboratory sources is heterochromatic, and the production of monochromatic light usually requires the use of refractive separative devices (prisms, etc.) or absorptive devices (filters, etc.).

SOURCES OF LIGHT

Practically all laboratory lighting is derived either from daylight or from electrically operated devices. Sunlight and skylight provide a spectrum which is continuous except for certain narrow atmosphere absorption bands. Skylight is sunlight which has been scattered by the atmosphere and is therefore influenced by the nature and texture of the atmosphere. When atmospheric particles are small, the short waves are scattered more than the long ones. This results in changes in spectral composition of daylight as the sun changes its position with reference to the atmosphere; e. g., the increase in red light at sunset. This change in spectral composition of natural light with the time of day is an important consideration in experiments using skylight as the source.

The most common source of "artificial" light is the incandescent bulb. In this lamp a tungsten wire filament is heated to an incandescent temperature by passing an electric current through it. The spectral energy distribution of such lamps depends almost entirely upon the temperature of the filament. Although it is possible to make lamps with a broad spectral response, the common types emit mostly in the range from red through orange and yellow, with a large portion of the radiant energy falling outside the visible spectrum. A crude approximation to daylight from an incandescent lamp may be secured from a blue bulb which cuts down the excess output at the red end of the spectrum. An important consideration in the use of incandescent sources is the close dependence of their output upon line voltages, for with some lamps a voltage change of five volts on a commercial main will make a clearly visible change in output.

Discharge and glow tubes are other major sources of light. These include the well-known neon and argon tubes, the light from which is due to ionization of the gas in the tube as a current is passed through it. The light from these sources is characterized by the presence of bands of color rather than a continuous spectrum; they respond rapidly to voltage changes (making them appropriate when a modulated source is desired); and they are economical to use. One similar source, the sodium vapor lamp, gives a nearly monochromatic yellow light; another, the very high-pressure form of mercury vapor lamp, gives a bright light of wide spectral response.

Fluorescent lamps are a well-known source of this general class. They are discharge tubes in the sense that their initial light, which is mainly ultraviolet, comes from the ionization of a gas, such as mercury vapor. This ultraviolet light then strikes the inside surface of the tube which is coated with a substance that fluoresces or gives off intense light when such light waves are incident upon it. These lamps are available with various spectral distribution curves. Other electrical sources of limited application are the arcs of carbon and iron. For further discussion of light sources see Evans (2) and Hardy and Perrin (1).

POLARIZATION

Because the wave motion of light is transverse rather than longitudinal, it is possible to make it vibrate in a definite plane, or to polarize it. From most sources of light the waves will be vibrating in all directions. By the use of appropriate polarizing techniques light may be made to vibrate in a single direction —such as up and down, or horizontal. Many laboratory applications can be made of this property. The most significant of these is in selective transmission in which it is possible to transmit waves vibrating, for example, in a horizontal plane but to block out waves vibrating in a vertical plane. A common polarizing material goes under the trade name "polaroid." Wollaston and Nicol prisms are common special polarizing prisms, which find applications as modifiers of the intensity of light in some types of photometers to be mentioned later.

REFLECTION, ABSORPTION, TRANSMISSION

In most practical applications of light the source itself is not viewed. Instead, a surface of some sort is the immediate object of vision. For this reason, it is essential to recall that when light falls upon a material, some of the incident rays are reflected from the material, while others enter the material. Those which enter are either absorbed by the material or are transmitted.

When a beam of light strikes a perfectly smooth reflecting surface, the direction of the beam leaving the surface follows the well-known law that the angle of incidence equals the angle of reflection. However, in most laboratory situations, the surface on which light falls is not a perfectly smooth reflecting surface; instead, the surface is rough. A plane wave striking such a surface is scattered in all directions—it is diffused by the surface. Similarly, very few surfaces reflect all of the light falling upon them. When the material of which the surface is made reflects some colors more than others, or is selective with reference to the wave length reflected, that surface appears colored. A red book when viewed by white light appears red because of its selective reflectance characteristics. A material which is not selective will appear white, gray, or black when similarly illuminated, depending upon its absorption characteristics.

Absorption of light by most materials is also selective in

the sense of being greater for some wave lengths than for others. Light which is neither reflected nor absorbed will pass through the material—be transmitted by it. If a transmitting surface is such that light passes directly through without being scattered, it is said to be transparent; whereas, if it diffuses the light, the substance is translucent. A surface which transmits no light is said to be opaque. References to the transmitting characteristics of a medium are often made in terms of basic coefficients, such as the *transmission coefficient* which is the ratio of the intensity of the transmitted light to that of the incident light. *Opacity* is indicated by the reciprocal of the transmission coefficient; and a quantity widely used in photography, the *optical density*, is equal to the common logarithm of the opacity. The *absorption coefficient* of a substance is the fraction of light transmitted for a layer of unit thickness.

Selective transmission is a widely employed principle in laboratory color control. When the illumination of an object or surface with a light of known wave length is desired, this may be accomplished in one of two ways. Since monochromatic sources are rare, it is necessary to use a heterochromatic source and either (1) break it down into its spectral components by means of a dispersion device, or (2) selectively absorb all but the desired wave length by passing the light through a transmitting medium (or off a selective reflective surface). Such selective absorption and transmission is the function of the color filters used widely in photography and light projection.

REFRACTION, LENSES AND PRISMS

Because the velocity of light is less in a material substance than it is in space, the path of a wave front entering material is refracted or bent toward a perpendicular to the surface. When the light beam is passing from the material medium into space, it is bent away from the perpendicular. A beam passing through a transparent plate with parallel sides will pass through the material with no change in direction. It will simply be displaced.

The situation is different when the sides are not parallel. Control over the course of a beam of light is made possible by changes in the relations between the two surfaces of a material through which the light passes. Two important arrangements of this type are the *prism* and the *lens*. In the common triangular prism the "entrance" and "exit" sides of the material make lateral sides of a triangle. When a beam of light enters one of the lateral faces, that beam will be bent toward the perpendicular to the face; as it leaves by way of the other lateral face, it will be bent away from the perpendicular to that face (Fig. 5 - 2).

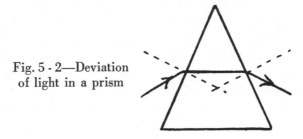

Fig. 5 - 2—Deviation of light in a prism

A lens may be likened to a prism with a continually varying angle (Fig. 5 - 3). A lens which causes a wave front to bend toward a single point or line is termed a *converging* lens; while one which bends light away from such a point or line is a *diverging* lens. Lenses find their widest laboratory use in optical

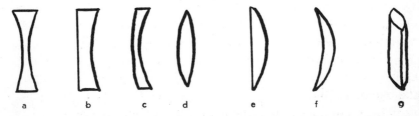

a   b   c   d   e   f   g

Fig. 5 - 3—Types of lenses: (a) double-concave, (b) plane-concave, (c) concave-convex, (d) double-convex, (e) plane-convex, (f) concave-convex, (g) cylindrical. a, b, and c are diverging lenses, and d, e, and f are converging lenses

instruments, which magnify and control images; and in concentrating, condensing, or diffusing light from a given source. The appropriate choice of a lens or combination of lenses for a particular design problem requires a careful study of that portion of optics which deals with the formation of images.

For a discussion of some of the above concepts as they apply to the physics laboratory note Strong (3). For extensions on the above see Hardy and Perrin (1) or Sears (4).

VISUAL STIMULUS SPECIFICATION

RADIANT AND LUMINOUS ENERGY

It was evident from the discussion of the electromagnetic (radiant energy) spectrum (Fig. 5 - 1) that visual stimuli are located in a restricted portion of that energy range. It is possible to describe any visual stimulus in terms of its location on the spectrum and the intensity of *radiant energy* involved. Location can be specified in terms of wave length; and intensity can be expressed as the rate of flow of energy past a given area of a plane perpendicular to the direction of propagation. Radiant energy is most conveniently measured in terms of heating effects and is designated in units of power; i.e., ergs per second, or watts. This would no doubt be the general form of specification of stimuli if the eye were uniformly sensitive to all wave lengths in the visual band. However, since the eye shows varying response to different wave lengths, the use of radiant energy (radiometric) specifications requires conversion to a visual reference scale. (See Table I.)

The concept of *luminous energy* is introduced to correspond to the concept of radiant energy and differs from it by the factor of the sensitivity of the eye. A related term, *luminosity*, is employed to indicate the luminous efficiency of a particular wave-length band of radiant energy. When adjusted to account for its ability to excite the eye, the term *radiant flux* is redefined as *luminous flux*. The basic unit of luminous en-

TABLE I*
COMPARISON OF RADIOMETRIC AND PHOTOMETRIC NOMENCLATURE

Radiometric term and m.k.s. unit		*Photometric term and m.k.s. unit*	
Radiant energy	joule	Luminous energy	talbot**
Radiant density	joule/m²	Luminous density	talbot/m²
Radiant flux	watt	Luminous flux	lumen
Radiant emittance	watt/m²	Luminous emittance	lumen/m²
Radiant intensity	watt/ω ***	Luminous intensity	lumen/ω (candle)
Radiance	watt/ω x m²	Luminance	lumen/ω x m²
Irradiance	watt/m²	Illuminance	lumen/m² (lux)

*Table adapted by permission from The Optical Society of America, Committee on Colorimetry, *The science of color.* New York: Thomas Y. Crowell Co., 1953.

**The talbot equals 10 million lumergs.

***The symbol ω designates one unit solid angle.

ergy is the *lumerg* and of luminous flux is the *lumen*. A *luminosity curve* is a graph showing luminous flux per element of wave length as a function of wave length, and it therefore relates radiant flux, visibility, and wave length (Fig. 5 - 4).

INTENSITY SPECIFICATION

Within the visual frame of reference an important distinction is made between the luminous energy received at a surface and the luminous energy reflected or emitted from a surface. The first is termed *illuminance* or illumination, while the latter is called *luminance* or brightness. Whereas illuminance depends upon light incident upon a surface, luminance (except for self-luminous surfaces) is a function of incident illumination and the reflection characteristics of the surface. The total amount of light that will be reflected from a particular surface depends upon the absorption characteristics and texture of the surface, the angle of incidence of the rays to the surface, and the composition of the incident light waves.

The basic unit of luminous intensity is an arbitrary standard, the *candle* or candlepower, maintained in bureaus of standards. It is expressed in terms of the luminous flux per unit of solid angle. Luminous flux represents the photometric measure of the rate of passage of luminous energy; with the basic unit,

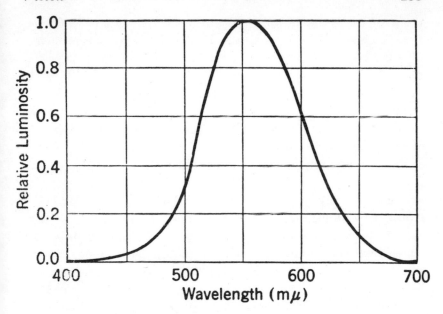

Fig. 5 - 4—Relative luminosity of the various regions of the spectrum. (By permission from *An introduction to color*, by Evans, 1948, John Wiley and Sons, Inc.)

the *lumen*, equal to the amount of luminous flux received on an area of one square meter on the surface of a sphere having a radius of one meter from a uniform point source having an intensity of one candlepower; or it is the luminous flux from a uniform point source of one candlepower given off in a unit solid angle.

Whereas the concept of luminous intensity is restricted to nearly point sources, the concept of luminance defines the luminous flux per unit solid angle emitted per unit of projected area of the source. Convenient units of luminance are the *candle per square meter, candle per square foot, lambert,* and appropriate fractional units. The luminous emittance of a surface is the total luminous flux emitted per unit area. This is the quantity commonly referred to as brightness and designated as luminous intensity per unit area, with the most common unit, the *lambert,* equal to the light uniformly emitted or reflected by a surface at the rate of one lumen per square centimeter. Millilamberts and microlamberts bear the conventional relationships to the base unit (one thousandth and one millionth). The *foot-lambert* or apparent foot-candle is a unit of brightness equal to the average emittance of any surface giving off light at the rate of one lumen per square foot. The average brightness of any reflecting surface in foot-lamberts will equal the product of the illumination in foot-candles and the reflection factor of the surface.

The density of incident luminous flux per unit area (illuminance) is measured in lumens per square meter, or *lux,* commonly referred to as *meter-candles.* A smaller unit, the *phot,* equals one lumen per square centimeter and is referred to as a *centimeter-candle.* The *foot-candle,* or lumen per square foot, is the normal incident illumination produced by one candle at a distance of one foot. With an average illumination of one foot-candle on a square foot of surface, the luminous flux upon the surface will be one lumen and the illuminance will be one lumen per square foot.

Retinal illumination differs from simple illumination chiefly with reference to structural characteristics of the eye. The most important of these is the area of the pupil. The unit of retinal illumination, the *Troland* (previously termed the *photon*), is defined as the intensity of visual stimulation which accompanies an object brightness of one candle per square meter and an effective pupil area of one square millimeter.

COLOR SPECIFICATION

Again in the designation of colors a division of the problem along lines of purely physical, psychophysical, and psychological units is appropriate. If physical energy alone is to be specified and studied, the spectral energy distribution can be adequately described in units of wave length. Such a specification has limited application to visual work until adjusted to allow for the spectral sensitivity of the eye as indicated in the luminosity curve (Fig. 5 - 4). For visual work, two types of color specifications are in common use. One is a simple and practical notation based on the psychological matching of a given color stimulus with reference colors from a color atlas, such as the Munsell Book of Color (7, 8) or the Ostwald color atlas (7, 10), only the former of which will be discussed here. The other notation is a more accurate technical standard based on the luminosity curve and on principles of additive mixture of colors. Each will be considered separately.

The Munsell color atlas.—This color reference standard is based on a color solid (Fig. 5 - 5) with a vertical axis extending from white to black surrounded by a series of horizontal axes in a conventional color circle. The specification of each sample is made in terms of three scales: hue, value, and chroma, with hue designated first, value second, and chroma last. Differences in hue represent successive planes passing through the

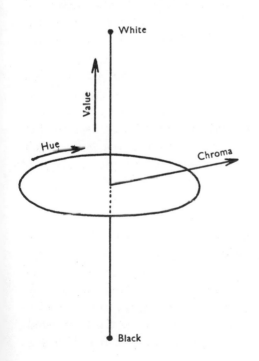

Fig. 5 - 5—The Munsell co-ordinate system. (By permission from *The measurement of colour,* by W. Wright, 1944, Hilger and Watts Ltd., London)

vertical axis of the solid. There are five basic hues (red, yellow, green, blue, and purple) and five corresponding intermediate hues (yellow-red, green-yellow, blue-green, purple-blue, and red-purple). To make smaller designations possible, the region between principle and intermediate hues is divided into ten subdivisions, with the central hue bearing the number 5. The resulting designation of hue includes specification by letter symbol (R, YR, Y, etc.) to indicate the general hue segment, and by a numeral preceding the letter to indicate the part of the segment. For example, the designation 4R indicates the hue of section four of the red segment.

The value specification of a color designates its lightness or reflectance characteristics in terms of an eleven-point scale extending from zero for black to ten for white. The specification of chroma, which corresponds to the saturation of the color, indicates distance from the central vertical axis of the solid in units which extend from zero for a neutral color (gray) to twelve for a saturated or intense color. A graphical representation of the three scales is given in Figure 5 - 6.

The general organizational plan of the atlas is to have successive pages represent adjacent plane sections extending vertically through the color solid. In its most complete form the Munsell Book of Color includes approximately one thousand samples. Excellent auxiliary information on the Munsell system, such as spectrophotometric specifications for the samples, is available (11). Among the obvious disadvantages in the use of such a standard are the possible effects of age and use upon the hues of the reference colors, and the lack of provision for standard illumination while the matching is being made. Equally important practical advantages accrue from the convenience in its use and the ready availability of such a comparison.

The CIE system.—The most widely accepted standard for color specification was set up by the International Commission on Illumination and is commonly referred to as the CIE system (until recently referred to as the ICI system, see refs. 7, 10, 2).

It is based on the well-known fact that any perceived color can be produced by an appropriate mixture of three other colors.

The three-color method of colorimetry involves the matching of a sample color by a mixture of three lights varying in chromaticity. The amounts of each (the luminance) is variable, and when a match is achieved these relative amounts provide a method for specifying the sample color. The choice of the

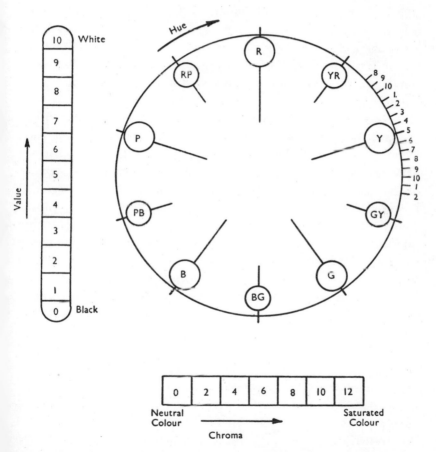

Fig. 5·6 –Hue, value, and chroma scales of the Munsell system. (By permission from *The measurement of colour*, by W. Wright, 1944, Hilger and Watts Ltd., London)

colors to be mixed is, to a degree, arbitrary; and for any choice of primaries a set of tristimulus curves could be drawn to show the relative amounts of each primary in the mixture. These relative amounts could readily be adjusted to proportions and expressed as tristimulus coefficients to the mixture. There could thus be developed as many sets of coefficients as there are sets of primaries.

The development of a standard requires the choice of standard primaries and the determination of the response characteristics of a "standard observer." Those selected involve a luminosity curve for the standard observer (Fig. 5 - 4) and a set of tristimulus curves indicating the amount of the three standard primaries required to match a unit amount of energy at each wave length (Fig. 5 - 7).

The choice of the particular set of primaries was influenced by the fact that some colors cannot readily be matched by an additive mixture (all tristimulus coefficients positive) of three components. Instead, they can be matched by a mixture of two components provided that some of the third component is added to the sample color. In cases like this, since the third component is added to the sample rather than to the matching mixture, it is considered negative in quantity, and the resulting coefficients which specify the color of the sample are computed on the basis of the net total (the negative component quantity being subtracted from the sum of the amounts of the other components). The presence of such negative values in a standard curve has disadvantages.

The set of tristimulus curves in Figure 5 - 7 are derived from unreal or "supersaturated" primary standards or components chosen to yield all-positive color-mixture curves. One of the three standard mixture curves is identical with the standard luminosity curve—a fact which is made possible by the use of the system of "derived" primaries. Since the luminosity curve is a linear combination of color-mixture curves, it can be used as one of the color-mixture functions in the arbitrarily chosen all-positive family of curves. The use of the luminosity curve,

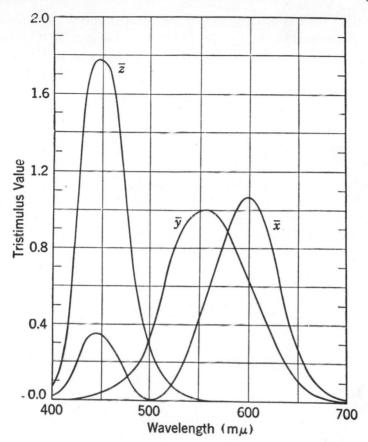

Fig. 5 - 7—The CIE tristimulus curves. (By permission from *An introduction to color*, by Evans, 1948, John Wiley and Sons, Inc.)

in turn, permits the luminance aspects of the other two curves to be made zero in the derived curves. In this way the ordinates of the derived standard color-mixture curves can be expressed in arbitrary units, such that the areas under all three curves are equal when the data are plotted on equal scales.

The tristimulus values of any sample of light are thus the magnitudes of the three standard stimulus components needed in a mixture to match the sample light. Each may be computed

by integrating the product of the ordinates of one of the standard color-mixture curves multiplied by the energy in the corresponding wave-length regions of the spectrum of the sample
of radiant energy. Chromaticity of the sample can then be specified by means of the proportions which each of two of the tristimulus valves bear to the sum of the three.

In other words, because a three-dimensional scale would
be necessary for the specification of all individual colors in
terms of all three tristimulus values, a simplified procedure
permitting a two-dimensional expression is employed. The
simplification arises from the use of trichromatic coefficients
which express the amount of a given primary or component in
terms of the fraction or proportion which it is of the total, as
follows:

$$x = \frac{X}{X + Y + Z}$$

$$y = \frac{Y}{X + Y + Z}$$

$$z = \frac{Z}{X + Y + Z}$$

Then, since $x + y + z = 1$ for all values of X, Y, and Z, a
complete specification for all colors can be made in terms of
any two of them. Given any two values, the third is determined
by the total of the three. The usual designation drops the z proportion and expresses each color in terms of the coefficients x
and y.

The graphical representation of this information is termed
a chromaticity diagram (Fig. 5 - 8). The y axis indicates the
y tristimulus coefficient or the fractional part of the Y primary
in the stimulus, and the x axis indicates the x tristimulus coefficient or the fractional amount of the X primary in the stimulus. The points in the curved line give the locus of the spectral
colors with their wave lengths customarily indicated in millimicrons. The values of these points can be computed by divid-

ing the ordinate of each of the color-mixture curves at the appropriate wave length by the sum of the ordinates of the three curves at that point. Thus the horizontal coordinate of each spectral color is the ratio of the ordinate on the X color-mixture curve (Fig. 5 - 7) at the particular wave length to the sum of the ordinates of all three curves at that wave length. And the vertical coordinate equals the ratio of the ordinate on the Y curve to the sum of the ordinates of the three curves at that point.

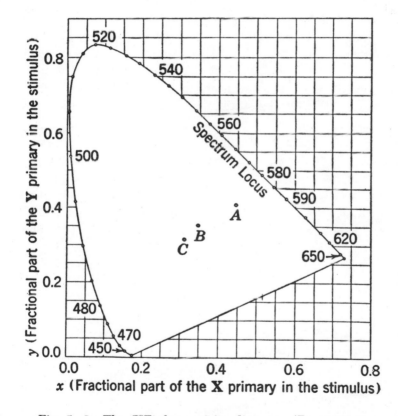

Fig. 5 - 8—The CIE chromaticity diagram. (By permission from *An introduction to color*, by Evans, 1948, John Wiley and Sons, Inc.)

The coordinates of a point specifying a color representing equal amounts in equal intervals of wave length throughout the spectrum is y = .3333 and x = .3333. A standard illuminant (point C) representing average white daylight has the chromaticity specification of y = .3163 and x = .3101. Another standard illuminant, representative of incandescent illumination, is termed A and bears the specification y = .4075 and x = .4476. Another standard filtered incandescent illuminant B of y = .3518 and x = .3485 was adopted for use along with A in colorimetry.

Other specifications of a given color can be made in terms of dominant wave length and purity. Both rest upon the choice of a point within the diagram which is achromatic. For practical purposes, this can be chosen as the point representing the white daylight illuminant, point C on the diagram. The dominant wave length corresponding to a given sample light is achieved by drawing the straight line determined by the achromatic point and the point representing the given color, and extending this line until it intersects the spectrum boundary curve. Nonspectral colors are specified by their complimentaries, the point of intersection of their lines through the achromatic point and the spectral boundary in the other direction. The purity of any light may be expressed by the relative distances to the spectral boundary and the achromatic point—the purer colors lying more remote from the achromatic point.

Much of the above discussion will be of limited help to the person who is interested in making the underlying calculations for excitation values in a specific situation. The direct method of calculation is tedious and involves integration. Therefore, the reader is referred to an alternate method described in detail by Hardy (12). For more detailed discussion and applications of the CIE specification see references 10, 2, 9, and 12. Much information is contained in the recent publication *The science of color* (7), by the Committee on Colorimetry of the Optical Society of America. Note particularly the references listed on pages 357-359 of that book.

STIMULUS MEASUREMENT AND CONTROL

Photometric Measurement of Intensity

Measures of luminance may be made by some form of *photometer* involving a visual or photoelectric match of standard and unknown lights. There are many different classes of photometers. In some instances classification is made in terms of whether the instruments are stationary or portable. Stationary photometers are most frequently installed in a dark room and used for making accurate intensity measurements; whereas portable photometers are built in compact lightweight form for easy transportation. When major concern is for illuminance characteristics, instruments may be classed according to function as foot-candle meters, illuminometers, and brightness meters.

A *spectrophotometer* is a specialized instrument for the measurement of luminance characteristics of monochromatic spectrum colors.

Another useful classification of visual photometric devices is based on the method employed in presenting and judging the visual stimuli. One type is the *equality of brightness photometer* which measures intensity by obtaining a brightness match between two surfaces—one illuminated by a standard source and the other by the source being measured. A second type is the *flicker photometer* which differs from the above by having the surfaces which are lighted by the standard and unknown sources alternately presented to the eye in rapid succession. Its use is most extensive in situations where a match is to be made of the intensities of two surfaces which differ in color. Matching the brightness of surfaces differing in hue is made difficult by the fact that the hue influences the judgment of brightness. The flicker photometer capitalizes on the fact that when two surfaces of different hue are alternately exposed to the retina in rapid succession, the sensation of color disappears, and when the illumination is equal for the two surfaces, the perception of flicker disappears.

Other devices which also may be termed visual photometers measure light by the ability of the eye to detect illuminated objects, or by the application of principles of visual contrast (13).

There are two essential features in the design of all visual photometers. One is a screen on which the illuminations being compared are presented and observed; the other is some system for control of illumination of the screen. The screen either reflects or transmits light, and the resultant brightness is observed directly by the eye or through some intermediate optical system.

A simple arrangement of screen and viewing system may consist of a translucent screen with a partition at right angles. The two sources of light are placed one on either side of the

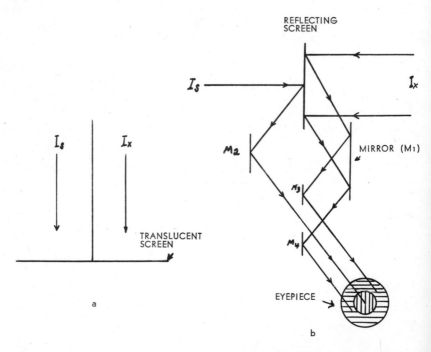

Fig. 5 - 9—Optical system for an equality of brightness photometric match: (a) simple screen, (b) concentric circles

partition, and the distance of the source from the screen is adjusted until the illumination is the same on both sides of the partition. This type of arrangement, illustrated in Figure 5 - 9a, has been widely used in studies of brightness discrimination with both humans and animals. Simple modifications introduce a wedge or a mirror to reflect the incident light upon a screen.

Another type, common in student use, consists of a screen made of a sheet of paper a portion of which has been rendered translucent by wax or grease. The translucent portion is often star-shaped to make the edges sharply defined. The screen lies in a plane parallel with the line of view, is simultaneously illuminated from one side by the standard source and from the other side by the unknown source, and two mirrors at angles with the screen reflect views of both sides to the eyepiece. More complicated devices employ lens systems for simultaneously viewing the illuminations of the two sources on the screen. A typical arrangement of this type, exposing concentric portions of a view field is illustrated in Figure 5 - 9b.

A flicker photometer optic system differs from the above in that some technique is introduced for alternately exposing the light from two sources to the eye in rapid succession, as is shown in Figure 5 - 10. The two sides of the wedge (G) at the bottom of the illustration are illuminated from different sources. The wedge reflects the light through a lens (L) and prism arrangement (Kk) into the eyepiece (A). Within the prism portion is an annulus (K) with a prismatic disk, the surface angle of which is cut so that, when it is facing in the direction shown, only the light from the right side of the wedge is visible in the eyepiece. When the disk is rotated 180 degrees only the light from the opposite side of the wedge is visible. In operation, some drive mechanism (usually a motor and pulley) is used to turn the disk at the rate necessary to obtain flicker.

ILLUMINATION CONTROL

Numerous methods may be employed for achieving a photometric balance. The most common illumination control varies the distance between the sources and the screen. In some instances the unknown source is moved while the standard remains fixed, or both sources remain fixed while the screen is moved to different positions with relation to the sources. Calculations are then made through simple applications of the in-

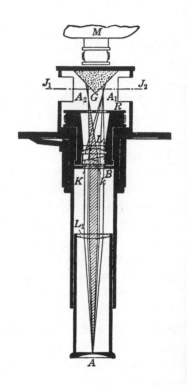

Fig. 5 - 10—Flicker photometer head. Description of symbols given in test. (By permission from *Light photometry and illuminating engineering*, by Barrows, 1938, McGraw-Hill Book Co., Inc.)

verse-square law—that the intensity of illumination varies inversely with the square of the distance from the source, expressed mathematically as the intensity of the source divided by the square of the distance. Then, since the photometer is adjusted until the illumination upon the screen from the known source is judged equal to that from the unknown source, the expressions for the equated illuminations can be made thusly:

$$\frac{I_x}{d_x{}^2} = \frac{I_s}{d_s{}^2}$$

or more conveniently

$$I_x = I_s \frac{d_x^2}{d_s^2}$$

or expressed as a ratio

$$I_x : I_s = d_x^2 : d_s^2$$

where I_x and I_s are the intensities of the unknown and standard sources and d_x and d_s are the corresponding distances. If the distance between the standard source and the screen is fixed, and its intensity remains constant, the expression becomes

$$I_x = Kd_x^2$$

This form of calibration is common in commercial portable equality of brightness devices.

The illumination upon the screen is frequently controlled by introducing some form of absorbing medium between the screen and one of the two sources. When this technique is combined with the distance method, the range of a particular device may be extended. In such a situation the equation for determining the intensity of an unknown source becomes

$$I_x = Cd_x^2$$

where C is the transmission coefficient of the absorbing material.

Another system for controlling illumination incident upon a screen consists of a rotating sectored disk (or *episcotister*) interposed between the source and the surface. The principle on which this device (Fig. 5 - 11) operates is that, if a portion of the retina is stimulated by periodic intermittent light of sufficiently short period, a continuous sensation results which is the same as would occur if the total amount of light received each period were uniformly distributed throughout the whole interval. In order to operate successfully, the intermittent rate must exceed the critical flicker frequency, which, in turn, is a linear function of the logarithm of the intensity. For a concise summary of the principles underlying the rotating sectored disk see reference 14.

Other devices for controlling illumination include dispersion lenses, variable iris diaphragms similar to those in cameras, polarization media, alterations in the angle of incidence of the light rays upon the illuminated surface, and variation in the intensity of the light source—usually by changes in voltage applied to the standard lamp.

Fig. 5 - 11—An episcotister. (Courtesy C. H. Stoelting Co., Chicago)

TYPICAL INSTRUMENTS

Stationary photometers.—Any of the foregoing devices may be employed on a relatively stationary optical and photometric bench. Such a setup is useful in making accurate measurements under highly controlled conditions and in preliminary studies where ready adjustment and interchange of components are desired. In a common form it consists of a graduated metal bar on which are mounted lamps for light sources, rotating disks or absorbing media for control of intensity, screens for cutting off stray light and otherwise shielding the stimulus, the photometric head (screen and viewing arrangement), lens and prism holders, and such auxiliary equipment as may be necessary for providing control of voltage impressed upon the lamps.

Fig. 5 · 12—A stationary bar photometer. (Courtesy Leeds & Northrup Co., Philadelphia, Pa.)

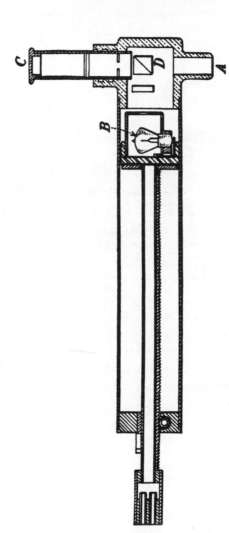

Fig. 5 - 13—The Macbeth illuminometer. (By permission from *Light photometry and illuminating engineering*, by Barrows, 1938, McGraw-Hill Book Co., Inc.)

A drawing of an optic and photometric bench is given in Figure 5 - 12.

Brightness meters and foot-candle meters.—Since the major concern of research workers in the visual field is for surfaces and objects to be perceived by subjects, rather than for light sources to be viewed directly, measurements are most often in units of illumination and brightness. Brightness meters are usually modified portable visual photometers, whereas the most common form of foot-candle meter is a physical photometer, or photoelectric cell photometer.

A *brightness photometer* differs from those already discussed only in that the source making up one-half of the visual field is replaced by a surface the brightness of which is to be measured, and a comparison surface rather than a point source is used. The Macbeth Illuminometer is typical of this type of device (Fig. 5 - 13). It consists of a photometric screen viewed through a telescopic eyepiece (C) and an aperture (A) opposite the eyepiece pointed toward the surface being tested. Light from this surface illuminates a portion of the screen, while light from a standard source falls on a ground-glass surface and is seen on another portion of the screen (D). The lamp (B) is mounted on a movable rod in order that the distance between the lamp and the ground glass may be altered. Movement of the lamp is accomplished by a gear which drives a bar calibrated in units of brightness. Measurement is made by pointing the instrument at the surface, moving the lamp back and forth until a match is achieved on the screen, and reading the value from the scale. A similar device which permits the focussing of the image of the object on the photometric field is the Luckiesh-Taylor brightness meter (15, p. 323). Here the match is made by absorption methods rather than by alteration of the distance of the standard light from the comparison surface.

Foot-candle meters are the most widely known form of photoelectric cell photometer and are used to measure illuminance (Fig. 5 - 14). Their chief advantage lies in convenience and relative independence of the human judge, on whose discrimination the results with visual photometers depend. The barrier layer (photovoltaic) cell is well adapted to this purpose because of the similarity of its spectral sensitivity curve to that of the human eye (Fig. 5 - 15). When used with appropriate filters these cells are capable of readings very similar to those obtained with the eye. The response curve does change with age and prolonged use of the cell, however; and frequent checking and re-calibrating is necessary to insure that the spectral sensitivity of the cell agrees with that of the eye.

Fig. 5 - 14—A foot-candle meter. (Courtesy Chicago Apparatus Co.)

THE MEASUREMENT OF COLOR

Spectrophotometry.—For industrial and physical applications, the most frequent measure of color involves a determination of the luminous energy of narrow bands of the spectrum contained in the sample light. This process is termed *spectrophotometry* and needs to be differentiated from the process of *spectroradiometry*. The same distinction between photometric and radiometric measures which was discussed earlier is relevant here. If measurement of the actual radiant energy of successive bands of the spectrum is made by a device such as a thermopile, the process is spectroradiometry; whereas, if the measurement is made with reference to the sensitivity of the eye, the process is that of spectrophotometry.

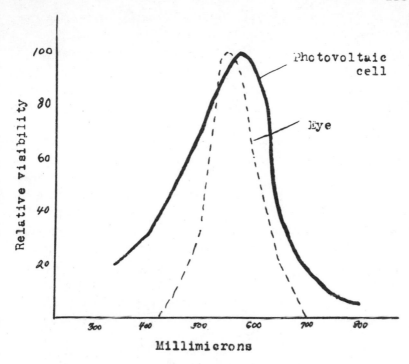

Fig. 5 - 15—Comparison curves of sensitivity of the human eye and a barrier layer cell

The essential procedure in spectrophotometry is that of breaking up a complex light into its spectral components and measuring the relative luminous energies of each band. Apparatus may be classed into visual and physical types, depending upon whether the matching is done by a human observer or by a photoelectric cell. In the physical types the cells act merely as a substitute for the eye, since human visibility is retained as the base. Where extensive measurements are to be made, photoelectric instruments have labor-saving advantages and overcome some of the weaknesses of the human observer. For these reasons they are extensively used in industry (10).

A *monochromator*, or device for picking up the light from the sample and making a spectral dispersion of it for presentation to the eye one color at a time, is a central part of the spectrophotometer. Dispersion is usually accomplished by some modification of the sixty-degree prism. A similar arrangement is necessary for presenting a comparison beam of light of known characteristics. These two sources are then thrown on a viewing field or screen for brightness matching by the eye or photoelectric cells. The match is made by devices for altering the luminance characteristics of one or both beams, frequently by means of absorption wedges and rotating sectored disks.

In this manner measurements are taken at a series of wave lengths throughout the spectrum. In each case a match is made between the comparison beams by the eye or by a photoelectric cell. In visual-matching instruments the intensity at each spectral level is typically indicated by a calibration of the intensity-control device in the comparison system; whereas, with photoelectric cells the output voltage is recorded and converted directly into a measure of light. A schematic diagram of a visual spectrophotometer is given in Figure 5 - 16, and relevant references are 1, 2, 9, and 10.

Colorimeters.—When the determination of color composition is made by direct matching of a color sample by color mixture or by measuring its tricolor characteristics without dispersing it into a spectrum, the instrument is called a colorimeter. Its essential features include a system for presenting a standard and an unknown color to the view of an observer or a photoelectric cell (7, 9, 10). The unknown field is illuminated by reflection or emission from the source being measured, while the other field is illuminated by a variable standard source.

Models differ in the manner in which the standard or known source of colored light is produced and varied in brightness and chromatic composition. Since a match is made upon the sample as it stands—that is, without breaking it up into its spectral components—some device for appropriate mixing of colors is incorporated in the standard source. Varying amounts of red, blue, and green primary sources are combined to produce a match. This may be done either additively—by means

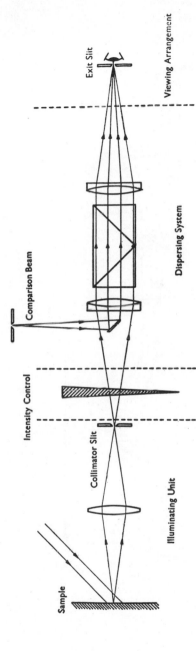

Sample

Illuminating Unit

Collimator Slit

Intensity Control

Comparison Beam

Dispersing System

Exit Slit

Viewing Arrangement

Fig. 5 - 16—Diagram of a spectrophotometer. (By permission from *The measurement of colour*, by W. Wright, 1944, Hilger and Watts Ltd., London)

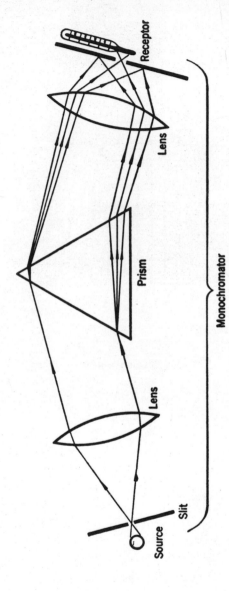

Fig. 5 · 17—A monochromator. (By permission from *An introduction to color*, by Evans, 1948, John Wiley and Sons, Inc.)

of a mixture of lights of variable intensity shining through red, green, and blue filters of known absorption characteristics—or subtractively, by selective absorption of necessary components from a white beam of light.

The match may be made visually, in which case an instrument is employed for presenting two fields, known and unknown, to the eye simultaneously; or photoelectric cells may be used to match the components. A somewhat different approach to the same problem employs three photoelectric cells. Each is adjusted to have its sensitivity curve match one of the three basic color-visibility curves. In this way the output of each cell can be made to indicate the composition of a sample with reference to a particular base color. A single photoelectric cell with a broad response curve can be used instead of the above three cells. When this is the case, three successive readings with different filters are required.

Color Control

Monochromators.—When it is desired to produce a stimulus light with great purity of color, a monochromator may be used to disperse the wave lengths from a white light source and to select from among the colors thus dispersed one for delivery to the eye or viewing screen. Such a device consists essentially (Fig. 5 - 17) of a collimator which gives a parallel beam of light from a slit, a prism which disperses the parallel light beam, and a focussing system for selecting a particular wave length and delivering it to a view slit or screen. These devices belong to a class more commonly termed *spectrometers*. A monochromator forms an essential part of the spectrophotometer (note Fig. 5 - 16). Spectrometers and allied spectroscopic instruments are produced commercially by physical supply houses. A monochromator with a camera substituted for the viewing slit is called a spectrograph; with a telescope replacing the slit, a spectroscope (Fig. 5 - 18).

Filters.—When production and control of the color composition of general illumination is desired, the most convenient

Fig. 5 - 18—A spectroscope. (Courtesy
Chicago Apparatus Co.)

arrangement consists of a source of white light from which all
but the desired wave lengths have been absorbed by means of
color filter. A color filter is simply a selective transmitting
medium. Such filters may be made from special glass to which
appropriate absorptive chemicals have been added, or, as is
more common, from gelatin film. A common series of the latter
type, the Wratten filters, consist of thin films of gelatin containing appropriate dyes. They are ordinarily available in this
form which requires special handling, or mounted between
optical glass plates.

The Wratten color filter series is manufactured by the
Eastman Kodak Co. Although the main purpose of these filters
is photographic, their use is not restricted to that field and over
one hundred different Wratten filters are available. Specification is by means of a code, and spectrograms and absorption
curves (Fig. 5 - 19) are available for the various specifications.

This information is given in published catalogue form (16) by the manufacturers. Of special laboratory interest is a series of "monocromatic" filters with relatively narrow transmission bands located at nearly equidistant positions throughout the spectrum (17).

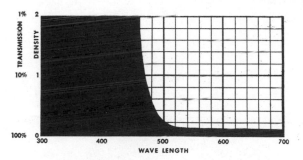

Fig. 5 - 19—Filter absorption curve.
(Courtesy Eastman Kodak Co.)

SPECIAL VISUAL APPARATUS

Ophthalmic Instruments

Many pieces of visual laboratory apparatus are made available by their commercial use by the ophthalmologist, oculist, and optometrist. While much of the equipment used by these persons is not used in psychological laboratory work (such as refracting equipment for fitting spectacles), some of it finds occasional use. In the latter class fall instruments for measuring acuity, color vision, adaptation, and the distribution of color sensitivity on the retina.

Acuity measures.—The most common visual acuity devices are the familiar test charts. Examples of these are the Snellen Rating Charts (Fig. 5 - 20) and the American Medical Association charts. While they do not yield measures adequate for all purposes, their practical advantages cause them to be used in routine laboratory screening operations. They are constructed of black letters (or figures) on a white background.

The size of the letters is made to correspond to equal visual size when each is seen from a prescribed distance. The standard distance is twenty feet; the next larger letters are such that, when they are viewed from 25 feet, they have the same visual size as the "standard" size at 20 feet. The largest letters are such that when viewed from 200 feet their visual size equals that of the standard as viewed from 20 feet.

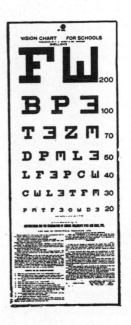

Fig. 5 - 20—Snellen visual acuity chart. (Courtesy Marietta Apparatus Co., Marietta, Ohio)

A visual acuity rating from the Snellen chart is secured from the ratio of the distance in feet from which a given line of the chart is just discernible by the subject and the distance in feet from which the same line of the chart is just discernible by a person with normal, or 20/20 vision. A person who possesses, for example, 20/200 vision is able to see at 20 feet the size which the "normal" person is able to discern at 200 feet. The A.M.A. charts use a similar index expressed as visual efficiency in percent, where 20/20 vision equals 100 percent visual efficiency.

For precision measures these charts have certain disadvantages. In the first place, they are made to measure the maximum contrast of blacks and whites. Instances are numerous in which measurements are made for application to problems of different degrees of contrast. Since visibility, as such, is a product of the form of the test object, different letters or figures have different relative visibilities even though the size, contrast, and illumination conditions are controlled. In addition, the perception of the figures is related to the light incident upon the chart, a condition which is difficult to keep constant.

Typical laboratory devices for measuring acuity depend upon the discrimination of an interspace between two parallel bars (Fig. 5 - 21), the opening (or absence thereof) in a circle or "C" figure, or the position of a grating of light and dark bands (15). In these contexts visual acuity is defined as the reciprocal of the just resolvable visual angle.

In between these precision techniques and the test charts are numerous types of acuity instruments. Two of these, the telebinocular and the orthorator (20), operate on the stereoscopic principle and possess an optical viewing system. Some portable devices, termed visibility meters, (15) consist of binocular viewing arrangements equipped with continuously variable absorptive screens. These filters permit the alteration of the brightness contrast of the object being viewed. In this way a threshold visibility may be determined and read directly from the apparatus, which may be calibrated in terms of relative visibility or relative foot-candles.

Color vision.—Many different devices for measuring color blindness are available from apparatus supply houses (19). One of the most common of these is the colored yarn sorting test, consisting of a large number of small skeins of various hues and a series of test or comparison skeins to which the smaller ones are matched by the subject. Such a test is convenient to use in certain situations, but is subject to error due to changes of hue with age and possible brightness differences between the skeins.

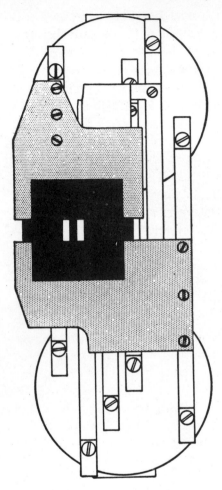

Fig. 5 - 21—Cobb visual acuity apparatus. (By permission from *The science of seeing,* by Luckiesh and Moss, 1937, D. Van Nostrand Co., Inc.)

Another popular class of tests employs color plates with a figure (or figures) made of colored dots. Typically, patterns of dots of one color are arranged in a background of dots of another color. The choice of the two colors is such that the color-blind person perceives no figures, while the person with normal vision does; or each may see different figures. Precautions are taken in the preparation of such color plates to introduce randomly dots differing in brightness but not in hue, in order to prevent discrimination on brightness rather than hue. Others use the brightness factor as the test; that is, two figures are present, one outlined by chromatic differences, the other by weak brightness differences. For the normal eye the colored figure will predominate, but for the color-deficient individual, the brightness figure will stand out. An example of this form of test is the Ishihara (18) (Fig. 5 - 22).

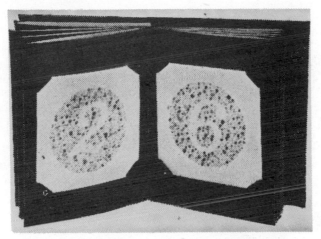

Fig. 5 - 22—Ishahara color blindness test. (Courtesy Marietta Apparatus Co., Marietta, Ohio)

For precision studies of color vision, standard surface areas exposed to lights of measured intensity and chroma are produced readily through the use of filters. By this means the components of color matches of individuals can be compared to those of "standard observers," and distinctions can be made between different classes of color-vision deficiency. Instruments constructed for this purpose are frequently called *anomaloscopes*.

Perimeters and campimeters.—A common demonstration in psychology classes is that which measures the way in which color sensitivity is distributed over the retina. The simplest instruments for this purpose are the *perimeter* (Fig. 5 - 23) and the *campimeter*. The perimeter typically includes a broad metal semicircular arc which may be rotated 360 degrees. At the center of the circle are a chin rest and a sighting bar arranged so that the subject may easily maintain fixation upon a mirror or sight hole in the center of rotation of the metal arc. A stimulus holder rides freely upon the arc, which is calibrated in degrees to indicate the distance of the stimulus from the point of fixation.

Stimuli with commercial instruments include red, green, blue, yellow, and white stimulus objects. Briefly, the use of the apparatus is as follows: as a stimulus object is slowly moved in from the periphery of the arc (or out from a central position), the subject, fixating on the center of the arc, reports when he first sees movement, an object, or the color of the object. A record is made on a standard chart of the points (in degrees) at which each color is correctly identified, and the region of achromatic vision is similarly delimited. By repeated measure-

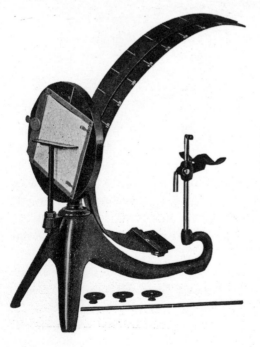

Fig. 5 - 23 — A visual perimeter. (Courtesy Marietta Apparatus Co., Marietta, Ohio)

ments on each of several axes of the arc, a reliable "map" of the color zones of the retina may be made. The blind spot may be located by recording the point at which small objects disappear temporarily in their course along the arc. Automatic recording perimeters are available, and in some research applications the simple arc is extended to a hemisphere.

Campimeters differ in certain essential features from the above. In the perimeter the stimulus moves along an arc and the eye fixates upon a stationary point, while in the campimeter the stimulus is stationary and the eye fixates upon a moving point. In this way the effect of the curvature of the retina is obtained by turning the eye with reference to the stimulus rather than by moving the stimulus. The subject's head remains fixed; only his eyes move. Many advantages result from the use of a stationary stimulus, since bulkier stimulus-producing arrangements may be employed. One of the most common means of producing color stimulation for this purpose is the color rotor. A *rotary campimeter* is a combined instrument permitting the advantage of either a fixed stimulus or a movable arc.

Other ophthalmic instruments.—The *adaptometer* is a commercial device for measuring the ability of the eye to adapt to low illumination. It has two light sources and a headrest. In administering the test in a completely dark room, a bright light is turned on for a given period of time. This light is then extinguished and a very weak light turned on behind a stimulus screen containing a movable figure—usually a translucent line on an opaque background. The subject indicates his ability to see under dark adaptation conditions by telling, as soon as he is able, the direction in which the weak stimulus line points, i.e., from "10 o'clock to 4 o'clock," etc.

Less commonly used are tests of astigmatism, blind spots, and ocular muscle balance. The *manoptoscope* is a device sometimes used to detect eye dominance. Instruments for observing the interior of the eye are the *ophthalmoscope* and the *retinoscope.*

Several visual test instruments are constructed on the

Fig. 5 - 24—The Ortho-Rater. (Courtesy Bausch & Lomb
Optical Co., Rochester, N. Y.)

stereoscopic pattern and are used for general optical screening.
Two commercial instruments of this type are the *Telebinocular*
and the *Orthorator* (Fig. 5 - 24). Each possesses a series of test
cards by means of which a variety of visual abilities are tested.
These include visual acuity, astigmatism, color perception,
depth perception, eye-muscle response, etc. One manufacturer
supplies a large number of such test series extending into problems such as remedial reading techniques (20).

COLOR MIXERS

A typical class demonstration of the laws of color mixture
requires adequate apparatus for the additive mixture of colors.
Probably the most commonly used device is the color rotor;
next, some form of colored light mixer; and, less frequently,

binocular and afterimage mixtures. Pigments do not serve the purpose well, since they mix subtractively rather than by addition of colors.

Color rotors.—The simplest color rotor consists of a motor on the shaft of which is mounted a metal disk and a knurled nut to make possible the interchanging of color disks (Fig. 5 - 25). Available color disks are made of paper, cardboard-backed paper, and plastic. A variable speed control on the motor is desirable. The most complex of such devices makes provision for changing the proportions of the different colors

Fig. 5 - 25—A color rotor

while the color wheel is rotating. One procedure for accomplishing this is as follows (21). Two disks are fastened to the end of one or the other of two hollow steel shafts which fit into one another. The outer shaft is motor driven. Two narrow parallel slots directly opposite from one another run through the middle of a section of this shaft. The smaller hollow shaft has a similar pair of slots cut in a spiral which makes one complete revolution. A steel pin passes through the four slots and is carried on the end of a third steel tube that runs inside the smaller shaft. Pushing the third tube in or out moves the pin in the slots and changes the relative position of the color disks fastened to the ends of the outer two shafts.

Colored-light mixer.—A typical additive light mixer is that in Figure 5 - 26. A box contains an opal glass screen, three

Fig. 5 - 26—A colored light mixer.
(Courtesy Chicago Apparatus Co.)

light sources in mounts which restrict the light to circular areas, removable color filters in mountings in front of the sources, and rheostats to alter the intensity of the light sources. By appropriate selection of filters and control of light intensities most desired mixtures can be demonstrated vividly. Another device based on the same principle mixes colors directly on a model of the color pyramid, showing changes in saturation and hue. See references 22 and 23 for construction plans for these instruments.

Binocular and afterimage mixtures.—When a different color is presented to each eye, as in a stereoscope, binocular fusion takes place. Mixture by this method is sometimes difficult because of the effect of binocular rivalry and incomplete control over the images reaching each eye. Commercial devices are therefore designed to minimize these problems. Afterimage mixers present no unique apparatus problem, for mixture is produced by projecting the strong negative afterimage of one color upon a homogeneous ground of a second color, thereby achieving a mixture of the second color and the complement of the first color.

VISUAL EXPOSURE CONTROL

In studies of vision, learning, and perception it is necessary to present a visual stimulus in such a way that the experimenter may control the illumination of the stimulus, the time the stimulus is exposed to the eye, and the point of fixation, as well as adjust for monocular or binocular viewing. Instruments for accomplishing this may be divided arbitrarily into two classes: those to present a series of stimuli for a relatively long exposure period *(serial presentation apparatus)* and those to present stimuli for brief controlled periods of time *(tachistoscopes)*. Some individuals have considered the term *bradyscope* to refer to slow-exposure apparatus, as contrasted with the term tachistoscope to refer to fast exposures (24).

Serial-presentation apparatus.—Numerous arrangements have been used in presenting stimuli to the eye in serial order.

One of the most popular of these is a revolving drum to which the stimuli are attached—the familiar "memory drum." As the drum revolves, driven by a gear or ratchet mechanism, each stimulus passes in turn before an aperture in a screen between the drum and the observer. In other instances, a revolving disk is substituted for the drum, or an endless band containing the stimuli is driven past an aperture. Some devices permit a stimulus card to fall slowly, or in steps, behind an aperture; or cards containing individual stimuli are mounted on a spindle in such a way that they may be pushed off the end one at a time at a controlled rate. For exposure of stimuli to groups of individuals, a projector, equipped with a motor or solenoid for automatically advancing the film, is convenient. Further discussion of serial presentation apparatus, including illustrations of memory drums, disks, and card changers, is included in a later discussion of "Learning Apparatus."

Tachistoscopes.—Devices for exposing visual stimuli for brief intervals of time were among the earliest instruments in psychological laboratory use. Several basic principles have been employed for controlling the exposure. Among these is the method most commonly used above in serial presentation apparatus, whereby the object being viewed is moved into and out of the field of vision. For brief exposures, the fact that the object is moving has obvious disadvantages. A second, more satisfactory, method is to have the stimulus momentarily uncovered by some form of moving screen. This screen may be a curtain with an aperture (like a focal-plane shutter in a camera) passing across the object (25); a rotating disk with an open sector which exposes the stimulus during a portion of each revolution of the disk (26); or a spring and shutter arrangement similar to that in a common hand camera. Among the difficulties of this type of control is the inability to expose all parts of the stimulus object for the same amount of time at the same instant in time.

The revolving sectored disk and the spring camera shutter are frequently used with a lens system for momentarily projecting an image of an object upon a screen (27). In recent years, an inexpensive device, a shutter with the trade name Alphax, has been available commercially for use with standard 35-mm slide and cut-film projectors.

Another principle by means of which short tachistoscopic stimulation is regulated is that of exposing the stimulus by a momentary illumination. This is accomplished by placing a rotating sectored disk between the light source and the viewed object (28) or by interrupting the electric current to an instantaneous light source. This form of control is used with a type of tachistoscope which has seen very wide application in psychology—the mirror tachistoscope (29). This instrument

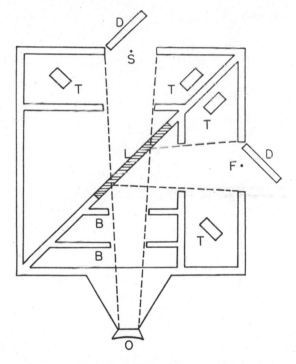

Fig. 5 - 27—Modified Dodge tachistoscope. (From Merryman and Allen [29] courtesy of the *American journal of psychology*)

consists of a viewing device with a piece of smoked glass (half-silvered mirror or lucite) inserted diagonally between the observer's eye (O) and the object (Fig. 5 - 27). This plate (L) is transparent when an illuminated object is behind it, but it functions as a mirror when the illuminated object is in front of it. The adjacent areas (T) provide for the illumination of either of two stimulus chambers (S or F). The alternate (reflected) field is used to control the fixation point (F) prior to the illumination of the second field, or stimulus chamber (S). Some device is necessary for turning off the light in the pre-exposure window at the instant that light is turned on in the stimulus chamber. Disks, pendulums, shutter curtains, and electronically controlled lights have been employed successfully.

REFERENCES

1. HARDY, A. C., and PERRIN, F. H. *The principles of optics.* New York: Mc-Graw-Hill Book Co., Inc., 1932.
2. EVANS, R. M. *An introduction to color.* New York: John Wiley and Sons, Inc., 1948.
3. STRONG, J. *Procedures in experimental physics.* New York: Prentice-Hall, Inc., 1946.
4. SEARS, F. W. *Principles of physics. III. Optics.* 2nd ed. Cambridge, Mass.: Addison-Wesley Press, Inc., 1946.
5. JUDD, D. B. Basic correlates of the visual stimulus. Chap. 22 in STEVENS, S. S. (Ed.) *Handbook of experimental psychology.* New York: John Wiley and Sons, Inc., 1951.
6. CHAPANIS, A. How we see: a summary of basic principles. Chap. 1 in NATIONAL RESEARCH COUNCIL report on *Human factors in underseas warfare.* Washington, D. C.: Natl. Res. Council, 1949.
7. OPTICAL SOCIETY OF AMERICA, Committee on Colorimetry, *The science of color.* New York: Thomas Y. Crowell Co., 1953.
8. MUNSELL, A. H. *A color notation.* 9th ed. Baltimore, Md.: Munsell Color Co., Inc., 1941. Also *Munsell book of color.* Baltimore: Munsell Color Co., Inc., 1942.
9. WRIGHT, W. D. *The measurement of color.* London: Adam Hilger, Ltd., 1944.
10. JUDD, D. B., *Color in business, science and industry.* New York: John Wiley and Sons, Inc., 1952.
11. KELLY, K. L., GIBSON, K. S., and NICKERSON, D. Tristimulus specification of the Munsell book of color from spectrophotometic measurements, *J. res. natl. bur. standards,* 1943, 31, Aug., 55-76; (Also) *J. opt. soc. Amer.,* 1943, 33, 355-375.

12. HARDY, A. C. *Handbook of colorimetry.* Cambridge, Mass.: Technology Press, 1936.
13. BARROWS, W. E. *Light, photometry, and illuminating engineering.* New York: McGraw-Hill Book Co., Inc., 1938.
14. BARTLETT, B. W. The rotating sectored disk, *Rev. sci. instrum.*, 1931, 2, 96-110.
15. LUCKIESH, M., and Moss, F. K. *The science of seeing.* New York: D. Van Nostrand Co., Inc., 1937.
16. *Filters and pola-screens.* Rochester, N. Y.: Eastman Kodak Co., 1943. *Wratten light filters.* Rochester, N. Y.: Eastman Kodak Co., 1945.
17. MACADAM, D. L. Colorimetric specifications of Wratten light filters, *J. opt. soc. Amer.*, 1945, 35, 670-675.
18. HARDY, LEG., RAND, G., and RITTLER, M. C. The Ishihara test as a means of detecting and analyzing defective color vision, *J. gen psychol.*, 1947, 36, 79-106.
19. CHAPANIS, A. A comparative study of five tests of color vision, *J. opt. soc. Amer.*, 1948, 38, 626-649.
20. *Keystone visual safety tests.* Meadville, Pa.: Keystone View Co. *Bausch and Lomb occupational vision tests.* Rochester, N. Y.: Bausch and Lomb Optical Co.
21. DIMMICK, F. L. An accurate differential color mixer, *Amer. j. psychol.*, 1932, 44, 798-799.
22. GRETHER, W. F. A simple three-color mixer using filtered colors, *Science*, 1943, 98, 248.
23. FREEMAN, G. L. A demonstrational color mixer, *Amer. j. psychol.*, 1932, 44, 346-347.
24. CHOU, S. W. "Tachistoscope" vs. "bradyscope." *Amer. j. psychol.*, 1930, 42, 303-306. DALLENBACH, K. M. The term "bradyscope." *Amer. j. psychol.*, 1930, 42, 306-307. ESPER, E. A. The bradyscope: an apparatus for the automatic presentation of visual stimuli at a constant slow rate, *J. exp. psychol.*, 1926, 9, 58-59.
25. EVANS, J. E. A tachistoscope for exposing large areas, *Amer. j. psychol.*, 1931, 43, 285-286.
26. FERREE, C. E., and RAND, G. A multiple-exposure tachistoscope, *J. exp. psychol.*, 1937, 21, 240-259.
27. NEWHALL, S. M. Projection tachistoscopy, *Amer. j. psychol.*, 1936, 48, 501-504.
28. KLOPFER, F. D. A semi-automatic bright-field tachistoscope, *Amer. j. psychol.*, 1953, 66, 105-109.
29. DODGE, R. An improved exposure-apparatus, *Psychol. Bull.*, 1907, 4, 10-13. KUPPERIAN, J. E., and GOLIN, E. An electronic tachistoscope, *Amer. j. psychol.*, 1951, 64, 274-275. MERRYMAN, J. G. and ALLEN, H. E. An improved electronic tachistoscope, *Amer. j. psychol.*, 1953, 66, 110-114.

CHAPTER 6

Other Senses

CUTANEOUS SENSES

The sensitivity of the skin to applied energy varies with the energy and the mode of application, to include sensations of touch or pressure, pain, temperature, and vibration. The chief energies include mechanical for pressure; mechanical, radiant, chemical, and electrical for pain; caloric for temperature; and mechanical and electrical for vibration. The class name for instruments measuring touch is *aesthesiometers;* while that for pain instruments is *algesiometer* or *algometers.* *Temperature stimulator* and *heat grills* provide temperature control; and *vibrators* or *pallesthesiometers* provide vibratory stimulation. In most instances, it is necessary to differentiate between stimulation which occurs at a point on the skin (punctiform stimulation) and that which covers an area of the skin (areal stimulation).

AESTHESIOMETERS

The simplest form of pressure stimulator consists of a camel's hair which has been calibrated to indicate the number of grams of force required to just bend the hair, for different lengths (Fig. 6 - 1). Variation in pressure is achieved by altering the hair length and thickness. Such a device, although simple, has many disadvantages. Careful calibration of the hair must be made frequently, for use and bending reduces the resistance of the hair to bending; and the determination of a uniform "just bending point" is difficult.

The most precise work with pressure has employed some form of weighted pressure point of metal or composition, lowered on the skin by an electromagnetically operated balance

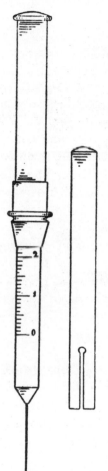

Fig. 6·1—Horsehair aesthesiometer. (Courtesy C. H. Stoelting Co., Chicago)

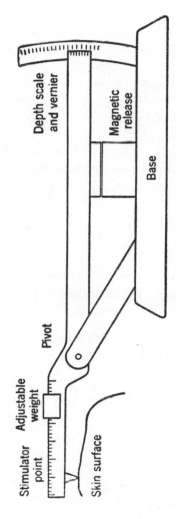

Fig. 6·2—Electromagnetic aesthesiometer. (By permission from *Methods in psychology*, by Andrews, 1948, John Wiley and Sons, Inc.)

arrangement (1, 2) (Fig. 6 - 2). Others utilized lever or solenoid arrangements whereby rigid stimulus points fall upon
the skin, with intensity controlled by the height of fall (3) or
the weight of the stimulus object (4). Investigations of areal
stimulation have used disks and similar objects (5).

A common laboratory pressure instrument is the two-point
aesthesiometer for controlling the pressure and spatial separation of two-point stimuli. It is used in measuring the two-point
threshold or the minimum separation distance of two pressure
points which may be perceived as two points rather than as one.

Fig. 6 - 3—Two-point aesthesiometer. (Courtesy
C. H. Stoelting Co., Chicago)

Inexpensive forms are made to resemble a drawing compass,
while more complicated forms provide detachable weights for
altering stimulus pressure and micrometer scales for reading
separation distances (Fig. 6 - 3).

ALGESIOMETERS AND ALGOMETERS

Mechanical stimulation for pain is sometimes made with
devices similar to the above except that the stimulus point is
made sharp and needle-like, rather than blunt; for a sharp point

is capable of giving deep stimulation without sensation of pressure (Fig. 6 - 4). Clinical measures of analgesia vary from this type to heavy pressure stimulation (6), temperature stimulation (5), and radiant energy stimulation (7). The radiant energy

Fig. 6 - 4—Algesiometer, needle type. (Courtesy Marietta Apparatus Co., Marietta, Ohio)

method (Fig. 6 - 5) has been widely used and has a number of advantages. The rays of a bright light are brought to a focus just beyond the surface of the skin, and intensity measures are made in terms of the intensity of irradiance as indicated by a thermocouple.

TEMPERATURE STIMULATORS

Studies of sensations of heat and cold differ with respect to whether areal or punctiform stimulation is made. Typical areal procedure employs a heat grill on which the subject rests the volar surface of the arm (or other body part) with the pressure of the body surface on the grill regulated. Most heat grills are constructed with tubes through which cold or warm water circulates. Both glass and metal tubes have been employed, with copper being the most common substance (8). In some instances, the coils have been wound around a core (9); in others, two systems of tubes were employed in such a way that either could be presented (10). Still others immersed the

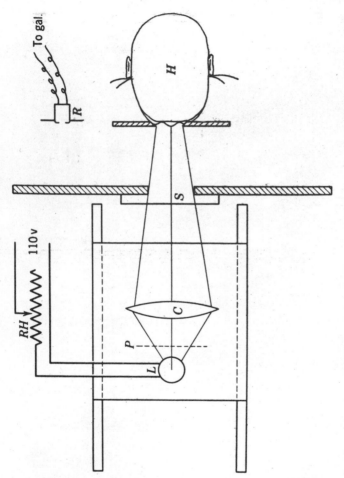

Fig. 6·5—Radiant-heat pain stimulator. The rays from the lamp (L) passed by exposure control shutter (P) are concentrated by lens (C) on subject's head (H) after passing shutter (S). Light intensity is controlled by a rheostat (RH); and a radiometer (R) may be substituted for the head for calibration purposes. (By permission from Wolff and Wolf. *Pain*, 1948, Chas. C. Thomas, publisher. After Hardy, Wolff, and Goodell [7])

contact metals (nails, screws, radio condenser plates, etc.) in warm or cold water, or heated them directly by a flame or resistance wire (11).

An example of a punctiform temperature stimulator (12) is shown in Figure 6 - 6. The pressure of a blunt copper stimulus point (E) upon the skin is controlled by a spring (G) of adjustable tension, and the temperature of the point is manipulated

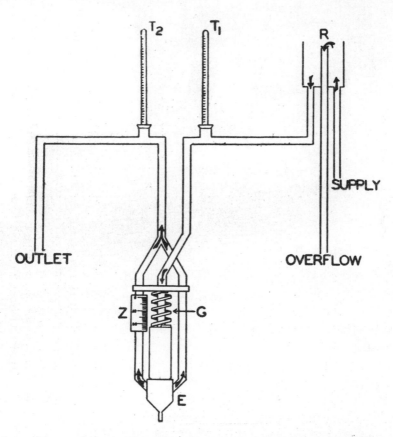

Fig. 6 - 6—Punctiform temperature stimulator. (E) stimulus point, (G) spring, (R) reservoir, (T_1 and T_2) thermometers, (Z) pressure scale. (From Hall and Dallenbach [12] courtesy of the authors and the *American journal of psychology*)

by a flow of temperature-regulated water through a chamber into which the copper point extends. The water is forced into the center inlet tube and escapes by way of the two lateral outlet tubes.

VIBRATORS

The perception of vibration has been measured by devices which range from tuning forks to direct electrical stimulation. The most common devices employ electronic oscillators for controlling the rate of vibration of modified electromagnetic or electrodynamic oscillographs (13).

OLFACTION

There are several outstanding features of instruments for the study of smell. One of these is the method for presenting the stimulus to the sense; a second is the system for quantifying the stimulus; and, finally are techniques for the control of relevant variables, such as the temperature and pressure of the stimulus. The class name of instruments for the measurement of smell senses is *olfactometers*.

EARLY TECHNIQUES

In the early periods of study of the sense of smell, many diverse techniques were employed for presenting the stimulus to the subject. Among the crudest of these was to place the subject in a room in which an odorous substance of measured amount was exposed. More elaborate procedure involved some sort of sniffing device, such as the open neck of a bottle, the open end of a funnel, or a small aperture in a box. In some instances the air was focussed by tubes and forced through the nostrils. In other cases nosepieces were used by means of which the nose was inserted into an isolated stimulus chamber. The most universal technique was that of evaporation or volatilization of an odorous substance on cotton, on filter paper, or in sealed vessels; and the setting up of some direct means of communication between the stimulus substance and the nose.

Quantification was a difficult problem. One of the most general techniques was a volumetric one in which the intensity of the stimulus was inferred from the volume of the gaseous substance of which the stimulus was a part. For example, a given or measured quantity of odorous substance would be diluted with a known quantity of air, under the assumption that the proportionate division of the stimulus would result in a proportionate decrease in the intensity of stimulation. In some instances the odorous substance was dissolved in a liquid solvent and the amount of the solvent in relation to the amount of the dissolved solid was used as the quantity. In other instances the amount of exposed evaporation surface was used, as, for example, the exposed area of filter paper from which an odorous substance was evaporating; or a measurement was made in terms of the size of aperture exposed to the nostril. The larger the hole through which the inhalation was made, the larger the intensity of stimulation. Other efforts at controlling the amount of substance inhaled employed volumetric techniques to measure the quantity of stimulus before and after a "sniff"; common devices of this type being a U-tube mercury gravimetric volume recorder.

The olfactometer which is present in most psychological laboratories, and is therefore most familiar to the average student, is the Zwaardemaker olfactometer (Fig. 6 - 7). This consists of two nasal tubes of glass projecting through a separation screen and connecting directly with the nostrils. On the opposite side of the screen a stimulus chamber fits over the end of each glass tube. This chamber is a long hollow tube, the inside surface of which is perforated. Within the tube is packing upon which the odorous substance is placed. The chamber is graduated in such a way that it is possible to read directly the amount of the interior or perforated surface of the chamber which is exposed to the air. The measure of amount or intensity of stimulation in this device is identified with the measure of the amount of the interior surface of the stimulus chamber which is exposed. This is read in centimeters. As it was originally designed, this measurement was to be expressed in terms of a limenal average or norm.

Many weaknesses of the early techniques have been determined. Most important among these are the fact that controls were not provided over features of the process which have since been demonstrated as very important to the sensation of smell.

Fig. 6 - 7—Zwaardemaker olfactometer.
(Courtesy C. H. Stoelting Co., Chicago)

One of these is the temperature of the stimulus; others are the pressure with which the substance hits the sense and the relative humidity of the substance. It was often possible for odors to escape from the apparatus, and some parts of the instruments were capable of absorbing odors, thereby changing the concentration of the stimulus. Many of the substances which were used for purposes of dilution had odors themselves and contributed to the stimulus odor. In general, there was poor regulation of the amount of stimulus which was delivered to the sense at any one time, for a great deal of early work hinged upon the quantity "sniff." It has been the concern of more recent workers to determine the relevant controls and to devise techniques for taking them into consideration.

MORE RECENT TECHNIQUES

One of the earliest improved techniques was based on the principle that equal volumes of gases at the same temperature and pressure contain the same number of molecules. The general apparatus consisted of a series of treatments of a stimulus air stream. The stream of air was forced by a pump; and it was purified and dried chemically before being passed through an odorous liquid. The temperature was adjusted, and the air passed through a nosepiece to the subject's nostril. The concentration was controlled by means of a temperature bath in which the odorous material was contained. The relative intensity was obtained from the vapor pressure and the known temperature at which the substances would volatilize. The apparatus was devised for a study in which relative concentrations rather than exact determinations were desired, and, for this reason, the unit was restricted to relative intensities.

In an effort to improve upon this general procedure, other investigators (14) employed three feed air lines; one for comparison purposes, another for dilution, and a third for bubbling through the odorous substances. These lines contained pressure measurement instruments and aperture or iris devices for controlling the amount of the substance from each. The units of intensity employed were the ratios of the odorous material to pure air, according to a formula proposed.

Another recent device consists essentially of a nosepiece and a bottle containing the odorous material. Control over the amount of odorous material to enter the nosepiece is obtained by a syringe. This syringe is connected directly to the bottle and injects into it a known or measured quantity of air. The outlet side of the bottle is kept tightly closed by means of a valve between the bottle and the nosepiece. In that way, the pressure within the bottle can be increased, due to the addition of air. Stimulation of the nostrils is made by opening the valve between the bottle and the nosepiece. The result is a small blast of odorous material entering the nosepiece. A modification of this technique introduces a second piston the function of which is to bleed air from the bottle. This permits pressure control and measurements on a volumetric basis. As used, these olfactometers failed to incorporate the advantages of the two previously mentioned for purifying the intake stream of air and controlling temperature factors (15).

A technique which incorporates the purification and quantification methods of the first two and the control of the quantity of substance emitted by the nosepiece of the third has been suggested (16) (Fig. 6 - 8). The air from a supply tank is purified and bubbled through a bottle containing the stimulus substance. It is then temperature regulated and pressure controlled. This stimulus is delivered to the nose by an automatic timing device which permits variations of the interval between stimulations and the duration of the individual stimuli. The pressure on the stimulus stream is kept constant throughout the stimulational interval by means of a device resembling a spirometer. Quantification in terms of the number of molecules in the substance is recommended. For a description of this apparatus, as well as a comprehensive summary of techniques in olfactometry, see Wenzel (15). Additional information on general technique, chemicals employed, etc., is summarized in Moncreiff (17).

GUSTATION

Requirements for the study of taste are similar to those for smell and include techniques for applying the stimulus to the sense endings and methods for quantification and control of the stimulus. In addition, it is often necessary to eliminate allied sensations of smell, temperature, and touch. Delivery of the stimulus is commonly made by special applicators, by

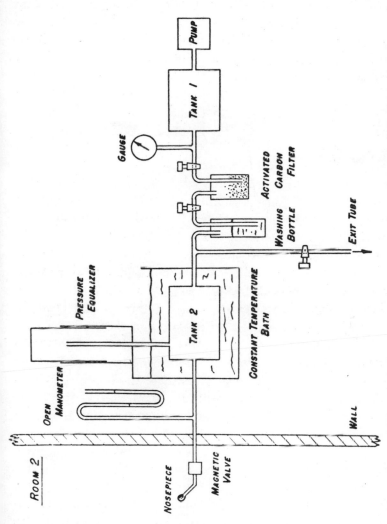

Fig. 6 · 8—Arrangement for studying olfaction. (From Wenzel [16] courtesy of the *Journal of experimental psychology* and the American Psychological Association)

dropping substances on the tongue from a pipette or medicine dropper, by sipping, or by small brushes saturated with stimulus solution. Direct electric stimulation is accomplished by metal or wick electrodes.

A typical applicator (18) consists of two parallel tubes fused into an open hemispherical bulb (Fig. 6 - 9), the aperture of which is 1.5 centimeters in diameter. Taste solutions are

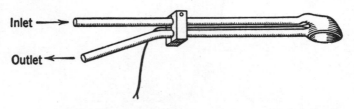

Fig. 6 - 9—Gustatory apparatus. (From Pfaffmann [18] courtesy of The Journal Press, Provincetown, Mass.)

passed through a temperature-controlled bath into the upper or inlet tube, then passed through the bulb, which is placed over the tongue in the desired area, and out through the lower or outlet tube. A thermocouple is sealed into the bulb, making possible the reading of the stimulus temperature at the point of application. To maintain a constant locus of stimulation, the subject's head and the applicator are held in clamps.

A similar apparatus permitting stimulation of the entire mouth is specially molded for each subject from thermoplastic wax or dental impression compound (19). The warmed wax is molded to the oral cavity, inlet and outlet tubes are inserted, and the material is permitted to harden. The inlet tube is located at the back of the mouth, and the outlet tube is forward so that the taste solution is carried to the back of the mouth and permitted to flow forward along the sides of the tongue to the outlet tube.

Quantification of taste stimuli may be made in terms of the chemical concentration of the stimulus substances in ratios of the number of parts of the pure stimulus substance to the number of parts of water as diluent. In some instances, a standard comparison substance for a particular taste may be employed in setting up a unit. An example of such a measure is the number of grams of a standard substance required to match a unit amount of test substance, with both substances dissolved in equal parts of water.

PROPRIOCEPTION

In the study of senses associated with postural and locomotor adjustments, the kinesthetic and static senses, apparatus has been most widely used for stimulating the sense endings of the semicircular canals. It consists chiefly of instruments for placing the body in controlled rotary or linear motion.

An early device, still used for this purpose, is the Barany chair, a sturdily constructed, straight-backed chair with arm-, foot-, and headrest mounted on a base in such a way that the entire chair assembly may be rotated. In a typical clinical examination, the subject is rotated 10 times in 20 seconds (with or without acceleration at each turn); then the turning is stopped suddenly. During the turning, the subject's eyes are closed and his head is inclined 15 to 30 degrees forward. When the rotation stops, the subject opens his eyes and looks straight ahead at a distant spot—ordinarily showing nystagmus in a direction opposite to that of rotation (20).

Several forms of rotating chairs and platforms, modified to permit motor drives, have been used. Some consist of platforms or chairs mounted on automobile wheel assemblies (21). Various drives include multiple harmonic cams, pulleys, and pneumatic-fan drives. One mechanism, designed to produce rythmic acceleration and deceleration in a sine pattern (22) employs a motor-driven drive rod which each revolution thrusts the chair by exerting a torque upon it. Other rotators provide rhythmical tilts of the head (23). Numerous animal rotation schemes are similar to the above.

Vertical movement and acceleration of the body are studied

by means of swings, tilt boards, or elevator-like apparatus (24). Much recent work on rapid rotary motion has used a human centrifuge. Aside from the use of these devices, stimulation of the vestibular apparatus is often achieved by injections of hot or cold water into the external ear (20), by direct mechanical stimulation of the exposed labyrinth of the canals, and by electric stimulation through the mastoid bone.

REFERENCES

1. JENKINS, W. L. Studying the skin senses, Chap. 9 in ANDREWS, T. G. (Ed.) *Methods of psychology*. New York: John Wiley and Sons, Inc., 1948.
2. NAFE, J. P., and WAGONER, K. S. The nature of pressure adaptation, *J. gen. psychol.*, 1941, 25, 323-351.
3. SIMPSON, R. M. An instrument for measuring intensity of pressure and pain stimuli, *Amer. j. psychol.*, 1937, 49, 117-119.
4. HULIN, W. S. A simplified electromagnetic aesthesiometer, *Amer. j. psychol.*, 1929, 41, 476-477.
5. HOLWAY, A. H., and CROZIER, W. J. Differential sensitivity for somesthetic pressure, *Psychol. rec.*, 1937, 1, 170-176. (Also) BROWN, T. G. A new differential aesthesiometer, *J. physiol.*, 1933, 77, 16P-17P.
6. GLUZEK, L. J. B. Dolorimetry in medical practice: the quantitative measure of deep sensibility and of pain. *Med. rec.*, N. Y., 1944, 157, 292-294.
7. HARDY, J. D., WOLFF, H. G., and GOODELL, H. Studies on pain. A new method for measuring pain threshold. Observations on spatial summation of pain, *J. clin. invest.*, 1940, 19, 649. (Also) FLINN, F. B., and CHAIKELIS, A. S. An improved instrument for the determination of changes in the pain threshold caused by drugs, *Amer. j. psychiat.*, 1946, 103, 349-350.
8. BURNETT, N. C., and DALLENBACH, K. M. The experience of heat, *Amer. j. psychol.*, 1927, 38, 418-431. (Also) CUTOLO, F. A. Preliminary study of the psychology of heat, *Amer. j. psychol.*, 1918, 29, 442-448.
9. TWITMYER, E. B., and FERNBERGER, S. W. Some new laboratory and demonstrational apparatus, *Amer. j. psychol.*, 1927, 38, 113-119.
10. BISHOP, H. G. An improved heat grill, *Amer. j. psychol.*, 1927, 38, 648-649.
11. SCHLOSBERG, H., and CARMICHAEL, L. A. Simple heat grill. *Amer. j. psychol.*, 1931, 43, 119. BARRY, H., and BOUSFIELD, W. A. A heat grill, *Amer. j. psychol.*, 1931, 43, 642-643. FREEMAN, G. L. A simplified heat grill, *Amer. j. psychol.*, 1933, 45, 344.
12. DALLENBACH, K. M. Some new apparatus, *Amer. j. psychol.*, 1923, 34, 90-94. (Also) HALL, N. B., and DALLENBACH, K. M. The duration of the aftersensation of cold aroused by punctiform stimulation, *Amer. j. psychol.*, 1947, 60, 260-271.
13. GELDARD, F. A. The perception of mechanical vibration, *J. gen. psychol.*, 1940, 22, 243-308. (Also) ARING, C. D., and FROHRING, W. O. Apparatus and

technique for measurement of vibratory threshold and of vibratory adaptation curve. *J. lab. clin. med.*, 1942, 28, 204-207.

14. GRUNDLACH, R. H., and KENWAY, G. A method for the determination of olfactory thresholds in humans. *J. exp. psychol.*, 1939, 2, 192-201.
15. WENZEL, B. M. Techniques in olfactometry: a critical review of the last 100 years, *Psychol. bull.*, 1948, 45, 231-247.
16. WENZEL, B. M. Differential sensitivity in olfaction, *J. exp. psychol.*, 1949, 39, 129-143.
17. MONCRIEFF, R. W. *The chemical senses.* New York: John Wiley and Sons, Inc., 1944.
18. PFAFFMANN, C. Apparatus and technique for gustatory experimentation, *J. gen. psychol.*, 1935, 12, 446-447. (Also) Chap. 10 in ANDREWS, T. D. (Ed.) *Methods of psychology.* New York: John Wiley and Sons, Inc., 1948.
19. DALLENBACH, K. M. Some gustatory apparatus. *Amer. j. psychol.*, 1936, 48, 504-507.
20. GLASSER, O. *Medical physics.* Chicago: Yearbook Publishing Co., Vol. 1, 1944.
21. TRAVIS, R. C. Perception and bodily adjustment under changing rotary acceleration: a new technique, *Amer. j. psychol.*, 1944, 57, 468-481. (Also) DALLENBACH, K. M. An inexpensive rotation table, *Amer. j. psychol.*, 1930, 42, 637-638.
22. TRAVIS, R. C., and DODGE, R. Experimental analysis of the sensorimotor consequences of passive oscillation, rotary and rectilinear, *Psychol. monogr.*, 1928, 38, No. 175, 47-48.
23. SPIEGEL, E. A., OPPENHEIMER, M. J., HENRY, G. C., and WYCIS, H. R. Experimental production of motion sickness, *War med.*, Chicago, 1944, 6, 283-290
24. ALEXANDER, S. J., COTZIN, M., HILL, C. J., RICCIUTI, E. A., and WENDT, G. R. Wesleyan University studies in motion sickness. I. The effects of variation of time intervals between accelerations upon sickness rates, *J. psychol.*, 1945, 19, 49-62.
25. GELDARD, F. A. *The human senses.* New York: John Wiley and Sons, Inc., 1953.
26. STEVENS, S. S. (Ed.) *Handbook of experimental psychology.* New York: John Wiley and Sons, Inc., 1951. Chaps. 29, 30, 31.

Chapter 7

Human Learning and Perception

HUMAN LEARNING

Instruments for the study of human learning may be separated arbitrarily into three or four divisions according to the type of phenomena investigated. Apparatus for verbal rote-learning studies includes mostly memory drums and allied serial exposure devices, while that for research on perceptual motor skills has many diversified forms ranging from mazes and pursuitmeters to mirror-drawing apparatus. Since the human conditioning methodologies are basically similar, conditioning apparatus differs mostly with respect to the response conditioned—as, for example, the eyeblink, GSR, and finger-withdrawal responses. Special arrangements for the study of problem solving include problem boxes, multiple-choice apparatus, and other situations accenting relations among stimuli rather than simple stimuli.

Verbal Rote Learning

Memory drums and allied apparatus.—The essential function of apparatus in studies of memory and rote learning is to control the order, manner, and time of exposure of stimulus material to the learner. The common name for this class of instruments is *memory drums,* the earliest forms of which were modified tachistoscopes (1, p. 108). One of the first specialized memory instruments consisted of a circular rotating disk driven by an electromagnetic ratchet mechanism (Fig. 7-1). A modification of this device (2), frequently used in elementary laboratory courses, permits the pushing of a lever which falls into a key on the ratchet wheel and moves the disk one place. The

190

disk is covered by a screen with a small aperture such that only one stimulus at a time is visible to the subject.

Other memory drums are built with a cylindrical drum on which the material containing the stimulus words or figures

Fig. 7 - 1—Ranschburg's memory apparatus.
(Courtesy C. H. Stoelting Co., Chicago)

is placed (3, p. 16) (Fig. 7 - 2). Originally, a continuous motor drive, geared down to a slow rate, was used; however, comments by the subjects indicated that the constant movement of the drum was distracting, and a series of discrete drum movements was introduced. This can be achieved through some form of ratchet mechanism, consisting of a ratchet gear fixed to one end of the drum and activated by a motor-driven pawl which strikes one notch of the ratchet each revolution of a constant-speed motor system. Additional features are included to reduce the amount of interfering noise from the drive mechanism and to permit variation in drive speed. Some forms utilize a wheel gear arrangement with rubber contact points such that a fan-wheel- or windmill-type drive strikes one of the keys each revolution, turning the drum one notch.

The front of the drum is equipped with a screen in the center of which is an aperture. The aperture may be a small slit, or it may have a slide which permits exposure of one side or the other (or both sides) of a relatively long slit. This type of drum is capable of handling either serial anticipation materials or paired associate materials. Paired associate materials

Fig. 7 - 2—A memory drum

are prepared such that on one line a single stimulus is presented; on the next line, exposed at the next interval, the pair of stimuli is exposed; then a single stimulus, then a pair, etc., yielding the necessary alternate exposure of single stimuli and paired stimuli.

More complicated drums achieve this objective by means of shutter arrangements which open and close apertures in the screen of the drum, alternately exposing single stimuli and pairs of stimuli, as desired. A drum which operates in this manner is termed a *paired associates drum,* and the principle on which one form operates may be seen in an illustration from Ray (4) (Fig. 7 - 3). The main cylindrical drum is driven by a rotary windmill-type mechanism striking rods protruding from the sides of the drum. A series of notched disks are

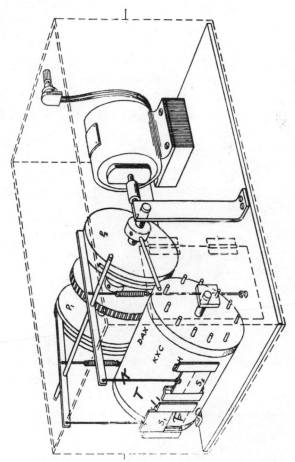

Fig. 7-3—A simple paired associates memory drum. (From Ray [4] courtesy of The Journal Press, Provincetown, Mass.)

mounted on the same drive shaft as the drum drive mechanism. Resting in grooves on the edges of these disks are levers, on the far ends of which are strings attached to sliding-door-type shutters in the screen. When these levers fall in recesses on the disks, they are pulled down by the force of their retaining springs, and the shutter is pulled up. As the disk rotates past the indented portion, the rod again comes to rest on a higher portion of the disk, and the lever rod is moved a distance sufficient to close the window. By appropriate notching of the disks the levers may be made to pull up and to close down shutter windows in harmony with the movements on the drum. Electromagnetically operated shutters are used more commonly than mechanical devices like this one but the principles are the same.

Fig. 7 - 4—A stimulus card-changer.
(Courtesy C. H. Stoelting Co., Chicago)

The usual method for employing such a drum is to have first one window open for a period of time, then to have the second window open such that both are open for a period of time, then to have both windows close until the beginning of another stimulus period.

Many other serial exposure devices have been employed. Since there has been increasing use of group methods for studying memory, the use of slide or cut-film projectors for exposure purposes has increased (5). Other *card changer devices* (6) achieve advantage from the fact that the stimulus material may be randomized easily for each trial. An example of this apparatus consists of a box and a spindle-drive mechanism on which rides a deck of stimulus cards (Fig. 7 - 4). The spindle is turned by a motor device, and, as it turns, a threaded "rider" on the screw of the spindle moves forward, pushing the cards forward at a constant rate. As the cards reach the front of the spindle, they fall off in turn, exposing each stimulus for an equal interval of time. As each card falls, it drops into a receptacle at the bottom of the box, which retains the order of the cards for the next trial; or, if it is desired, the cards may be shuffled between trials to randomize the order. Among the disadvantages of this device is the noise which accompanies the dropping of the cards.

Some general factors with regard to the use of rote-learning equipment.—Materials employed with memory drums are varied. Among the earliest were the well-known nonsense materials, which include nonsense syllables, made up of a vowel between two consonants; consonant syllables, made up of three or more consonants; number series; and unfamiliar materials, such as Chinese characters and specially constructed new languages. In the use of this type of material the investigations of Glaze, Witmer, and Hull in calibrating the associative value of nonsense material are often referred to; see (7) (8). Their calibrations were obtained by asking subjects to indicate the associations suggested by the syllables and by trying the syllables in learning situations. These methods have recently been extended through the use of scaling techniques with both meaningless and meaningful materials, in an effort to find an objective measure of association value and other relevant characteristics. Among meaningful verbal materials are single words, the most common of which are two-syllable adjectives or four-letter verbs, and selections of prose or poetry, common in studies with the method of complete presentation.

Considerable care is necessary in making up lists of materials to be learned, and the procedure for selecting words and preparing lists has become somewhat standardized among workers in this area. For example, in the construction of a list of adjectives to be learned by the paired-associates method, some of the "rules" adhered to include: that they be the correct part of speech and the desired number of syllables; that their level of difficulty, familiarity, or commonness be approximately the same, as judged from a word-list source, such as that of Thorndike; that the initial letter of any member of a given list be used not more than once in a list, if possible; that a given suffix appear more than once in a list if desired, but that each of the members of two successive pairs end with a different suffix; that the two initial letters of the items of a given pair should not be successive letters of the alphabet; that members of a given pair or in successive pairs not be synonyms or antonyms; that two items should not be paired if they suggest any paired usage, such as perfect—lovely; and that items used together should never be sonorous, an example of which would be the pair lawless—awful. These principles are representative of the considerations given to the materials in making up a list.

Other considerations are of importance, as, for example, the amount of time the syllable or word is exposed. This is also fairly standardized, and is based upon previous research under the specific conditions of interest. The most common speeds for memory drums range from 1 to 5 seconds, with the most widely used rate as 2 to 3 seconds per syllable. For further discussion of these methodological matters see references 3, 7, 8, and 9.

PERCEPTUAL MOTOR LEARNING

Mazes.—The oldest device for studying perceptual motor skills is the maze, of which there are many forms for use with humans and an even greater number for studying learning with animals. All have in common the presentation of a varied path from a starting point to a goal. Along the path are placed a certain number of blind alleys branching from the correct path. Maze descriptions are often made in terms of a general shape of the path. Two of these are the multiple-T and the multiple-Y mazes, so named because of the similarity of their choice points to these letters.

Among the most commonly used forms are stylus and finger mazes (Fig. 7-5). In the stylus maze the path is cut from a heavy material, such as metal or hardwood, leaving a

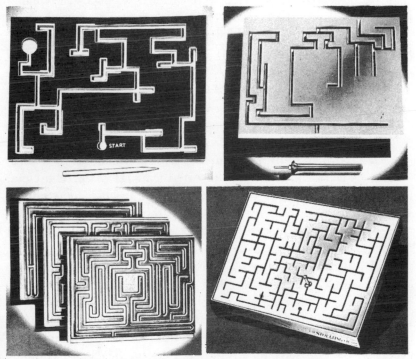

Fig. 7-5—Human stylus and finger mazes.
(Courtesy C. H. Stoelting Co., Chicago)

groove in which the stylus rides. The path is ordinarily a slot cut completely through the material in order that paper may be inserted below the maze, permitting a pencil to be used as a stylus to provide on the paper a continuous record of the course through the maze. Finger mazes are constructed with some material such as wire raised from a base material a sufficient amount that the subject may trace the path with his finger. In both the examples above, the subject completes the maze while blindfolded. A modification of the simple stylus maze employs two mazes, one above the other, and is termed a two-story maze. Three-dimensional mazes made of pipe and capable of paths in any of the three directions have also been used.

Some mazes incorporate the advantages of electrical scoring systems and are termed electrical mazes. Electric recording can be accomplished in stylus-type mazes by means of a metal contact built into the bottom of the path, so that, when the subject is on the correct path, contact is completed through the stylus; and when he gets off the correct path, the circuit is broken. The bolthead maze (10) consists of a series of bolt-heads uniformly placed on a baseboard and connected beneath the base with wires to form a systematic path or pattern of "correct" boltheads. The subject must learn to select with an electric contact stylus the correct boltheads from among many on the board. A similar instrument is made of holes in a baseboard beneath which may be inserted a metal plate. The metal plate contains the correct pattern, such that, when the stylus is inserted through a hole and strikes the metal plate, contact through the stylus closes a circuit; when the stylus is lifted or inserted in a hole which is incorrect, the circuit remains open.

In all these instances the circuit may be made to operate a light bulb, or buzzer, in order that the subject is able to see or be notified when he makes an incorrect response; it may be employed to activate a counter such that errors are summated; or it may be used to activate a timer and record the amount of time on the correct path or in a cul-de-sac. The most common methods of measuring performance on human mazes are in terms of the number of trials (or the amount of time) required to reach a criterion and the number of errors made in a similar period.

A maze widely used in undergraduate psychology classes is the punch maze, made from a hard material, such as pressed-wood or bakelite (11). A board with two rows of evenly spaced holes is placed on top of a second similar board which contains a "correct" pattern of holes from among the complete number. In working his way up or down the board, the subject must learn which member of each pair is the correct choice with reference to the key. A record of his trials is obtained by inserting a piece of paper between the boards and moving this paper a certain distance with each trial. When the correct response is made, the stylus will punch through the paper, and when an error is made, an indentation will occur.

Other types of mazes include those made large enough for a man to pass through, or full-size mazes. Paper and pencil mazes, including line mazes and letter mazes made with a typewriter, find extensive use, and even mazes made of common buttons have been used. The bulk of recent studies with the maze as an instrument of research has been with animals. There have also been numerous studies of reliability of the maze as a learning instrument for use with both humans and animals.

Pursuitmeter.—A very popular device for studying motor learning is the rotary pursuit apparatus or the pursuitmeter (Fig. 7 - 6). It is recommended by some as being only slightly susceptible to verbal control and hence as a fairly "pure" measure of perceptual motor skill independent of verbal factors. It consists (12, pp. 329 - 350) of a circular disk of approximately 11 inches in diameter rotating at a constant speed (most frequently one cycle per second), much in the fashion of a phonograph turntable. On the disk, placed approximately 3 inches from the center, is a round brass target mounted flush in the surface of the disk. A stylus with flexible handle is employed by the subject in trying to maintain contact between the tip

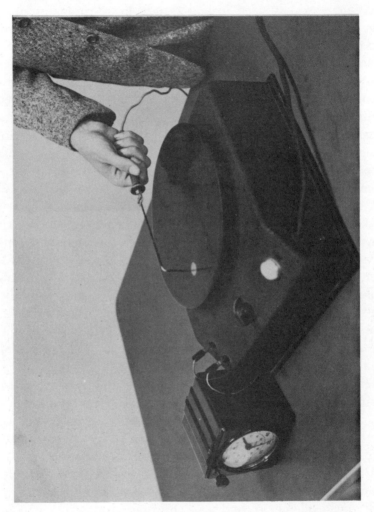

Fig. 7 · 6—A pursuitmeter

of the stylus and the brass target disk on the revolving turn-table.

The most common measure of performance is that of time spent in contact with the disk, although other measures, such as the number of strikes or hits, may be employed. The circuit to the timer or counter is made through the stylus and the contact disk or target. There are modifications of this fairly standard model which permit variations in speed, forward and backward drive, or irregular operation. One, termed an epi-cycloid meter, has the target operate in an eccentric manner by having the disk rotate around a noncentralized shaft. This disk in its commercial form (Marietta Apparatus Co., Marietta, Ohio) records the time off the target, for the target disk is insulated and the remainder of the turntable is a contact plate. Similar devices employ a linear pursuit skill such as is re-

Fig. 7 - 7—Mirror drawing apparatus.
(Courtesy C. H. Stoelting Co., Chicago)

quired in tracking a falling object. Others involve pursuit of a pendulum.

Mirror drawing.—A common classroom demonstration of motor learning, particularly with reference to transfer effects, uses the mirror-drawing apparatus (Fig. 7 - 7). The essential feature of the instrument is a stimulus board the image from which falls on a plane mirror which the subject views and endeavors to trace. His hand is kept from his view by a screen, and the only way that he can follow the course of his tracing is by means of the mirror. The reversing effect of the mirror requires him to. make movements contrary to his usual motor habits (1, pp. 40 - 47).

Less standard devices for studying motor learning include dart-throwing and target-shooting skills; tasks similar to office-machine practice, typing and shorthand; learning of code in telegraphy; and card sorting. Numerous psychomotor tests have been used as a basis for the study of motor skills (12).

PROBLEM SOLVING

Many investigations of learning have stressed the situation in which an individual is confronted with a problem within which there are certain stimulus relations he does not perceive at the outset. His job is to distinguish the necessary relations, thereby achieving a solution to the problem; or he must grasp a principle according to which the stimuli are organized. Problems range from mechanical puzzles (13), complicated puzzle boxes (14), and card-sorting and block-separating tasks (15), to apparatus arrangements for the study of higher mental processes, reasoning and thinking, an example of which provides the subject with a series of parts or individual components to a complete solution and requires him to discover the way the components combine (16).

Another common type of instrument in this general category is the *multiple-choice apparatus*, in which the individual has to apply principles or discover underlying generalizations in making a choice of a single stimulus from a field of stimuli.

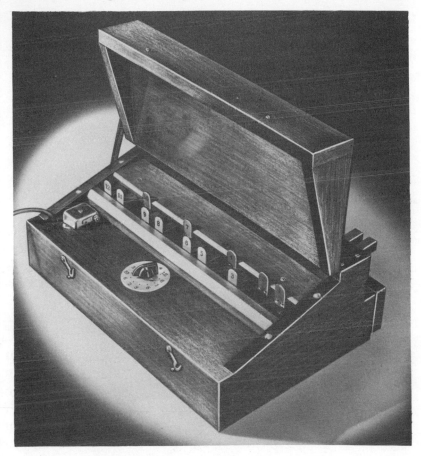

Fig. 7 - 8—Yerkes multiple choice apparatus. (Courtesy C.H.Stoelting Co., Chicago)

A series of numbers, letters, or objects is presented to the subject, and his job is to choose one or more according to a principle set up by the experimenter. An example of this class is the Yerkes multiple-choice box (17) (Fig. 7 - 8). In this apparatus the subject is confronted by a series of keys bearing numbers from one to twelve. One of these keys is the correct one, and the subject is informed of that fact. He knows when he hits the correct key, for this causes a buzzer to sound. The experimenter, behind the apparatus, can set it in such a way that any of the keys is correct by placing an electrical contact in the appropriate jack on a control panel. As the subject presses a key, a corresponding lamp flashes on the experimenter's control panel. The particular stimulus key which is correct is made to follow some relationship of a desired degree of complexity, as, for example, "two to the left of the first, or previous one." A more recent type of problem-solving (serial-learning) apparatus uses a series of relays and switches to confront the subject with a series of interrelated visual stimuli (18).

HUMAN CONDITIONING

Basic apparatus problems.—The function of instruments in human classical conditioning is basically the same for many different classes of responses conditioned: a conditioned stimulus of known characteristics must be presented; an unconditioned stimulus, also of known characteristics must be introduced; control must be maintained over the time between the stimuli and the time that each stimulus is on; and an appropriate recording of stimuli and responses is necessary. Typical unconditioned stimuli and the various means of eliciting unconditioned responses, as well as the variety of stimuli which have been employed as conditioned stimuli, are listed elsewhere (19). In general, the measures to be recorded depend upon the means for inferring learning. These may include amplitude of response, latency of response, or the number or per cent of correct responses in a given block of trials.

Eyelid conditioning.—Many systems have been employed for administering an unconditioned stimulus for the eyeblink response. One of these, the air puff, may employ a valve behind which a given pressure is built up, or a U-tube equipped with a mercury column which is elevated a certain distance and maintained at that level electromagnetically. At the instance that the stimulus is to be given, the mercury is released and falls to its natural level in the U-tube, forcing a measured amount of air through a tube to the eye of the subject. Another method employs a light shock to the cheek just below the eye. In other instances a sound of sufficient intensity to produce startle is used to produce an eyeblink, as is a winking glass consisting of a transparent glass plate in front of the subject's face, to which a hammer falls creating an avoidance blink. Other devices include a light hammer, electromagnetically operated, which taps the region of the face just below the eye.

Numerous conditioned stimuli have been used with this response. Time controls may be any of those mentioned earlier in the discussion of timing apparatus; the most common are electronic timers and constant-speed motor devices using micro-switches or contact plates.

Recording of the eyeblink response has been accomplished by many means, each of which requires care to avoid distortion of the response studied. One method takes action potentials from the muscles of the eyelid. Another has a light stylus attached to the lid of the eye to interrupt a beam of light to a photokymograph. A light hair has been attached to the eyelid to operate a very light mechanically coupled recording stylus. Pneumatic devices have been employed in which a light lever conveyed the movement of the eyelid to a receiving tambour, and a mirror has been fixed to the lid or to a stylus on the lid for mirror recording on a photokymograph. Electric contacts have been made and broken by a light stylus attached to the lid such that a light wire would slide across two contact points as the lid closed.

GSR conditioning.—The most common unconditioned stimulus in studies of the galvanic skin responses has been an electric shock administered from an appropriate stimulational device, although any stimulus which is capable of evoking startle responses or apprehension may be employed to produce the response. Emotionally toned words and pictures have been used. The conditioned stimuli again vary widely, and time relations are obtained in a fashion similar to that mentioned

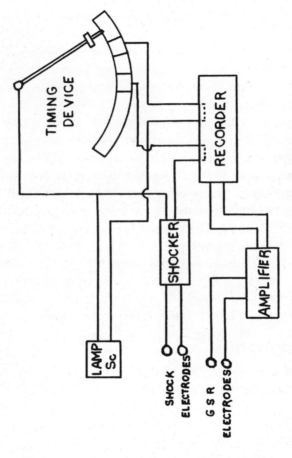

Fig. 7 - 9—Block diagram of GSR conditioning apparatus

in connection with eyelid work. Recording involves a combination of the general problems considered in any recording situation and the more extensive problem involved in the measurement of the galvanic skin response, a separate consideration of which is given in a later section. A block diagram of a typical galvanic skin response conditioning apparatus is given in Figure 7 - 9.

Withdrawal conditioning.—The most common form of withdrawal response used in human conditioning is the withdrawal of the finger from an unconditioned stimulus of an electric shock. It has been employed as a response capable of voluntary control, and, of the methods considered here, is the only one permitting avoidance conditioning; for the subject may be taught to avoid the shock by withdrawing at the onset of the conditioned stimulus. No novel equipment problems are introduced, although many techniques other than shock, such as falling hammers or weights, have been used to produce an unconditioned stimulus. The method is popular for class demonstration of the conditioning process, and several apparatus descriptions for this purpose have been published; e.g. (20, 21).

PERCEPTION

VISUAL SPACE PERCEPTION

Stereoscopes and allied instruments.—The study of binocular disparity as a factor in space perception has led to wide use of stereoscopic devices. Briefly, a *stereoscope* is an instrument for presenting two different images, one to each eye, simultaneously. Two pictures or drawings of the same object from slightly different positions of view are shown, one to the left eye and the other to the right eye. This is done in such a way that appropriate parts of the image are received by corresponding retinal points, and a single object is observed with the characteristic depth effect.

In the common form of stereoscope (Fig. 7 - 10), refract-

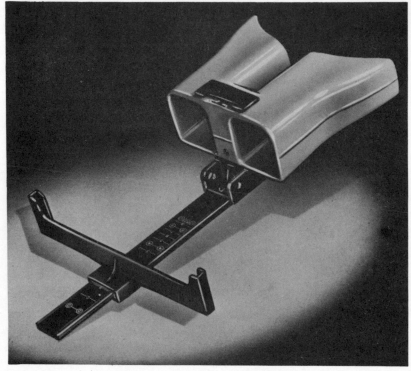

Fig. 7 - 10—Brewster stereoscope.
(Courtesy C. H. Stoelting Co., Chicago)

ing prisms are placed in front of the eyes in such a way that rays from the objects are appropriately bent to permit the subject to converge and accommodate upon the figure and bring it into clear focus, and a partition or screen prevents each eye from viewing the object on the other side. Standard sets of stereograms are available for use with these devices in demonstrating the principles of binocular disparity (3, 22). Other varieties of stereoscopes employ mirrors instead of prisms; plane mirrors are placed at angles to the line of sight and reflect the image from laterally placed diagrams or pictures. With such an arrangement, control over convergence and accommodation is possible.

A modification of the mirror stereoscope, termed a *tele-stereoscope,* gives an exaggerated depth effect by increasing the degree of disparity in viewing real objects. In this instrument (Fig. 7 - 11) the pictures are replaced by a second set of mirrors which reflect the image of a single real object. By increasing the separation distance of these mirrors, an effect equivalent to increasing the interocular distance is achieved. This procedure is reversed in an *iconoscope,* with the result that disparity

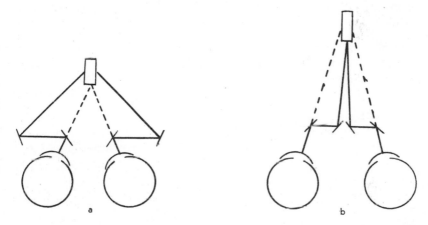

Fig. 7 - 11—Modified stereoscopes: (a) telestereoscope, (b) iconoscope

is reduced. By placing the "image-reflecting" mirrors inside of the "sighting" mirrors, the two retinal images are made practically alike—that is, as if interocular distance were reduced. Similar arrangements of mirrors may be used for reversing the binocular disparity by rotating the images 180 degrees, or in other ways altering the delivery of visual images to the eye. Such devices are termed *pseudoscopes.*

Several test-type instruments are constructed on the stereoscopic pattern and are used for general optical screening. Two commercial instruments of this type, the telebinocular and orthorator, were mentioned previously (see "Vision"). Each uses a series of test cards to rate a variety of visual abilities—

such as visual acuity, astigmatism, color perception, depth perception, and eye-muscle response—as well as special visual skills, like reading.

Accommodation and convergence apparatus.—The study of nonvisual cues to depth perception has led to the design of numerous instruments. The problem involved is a complex one —that of eliminating visual cues while retaining necessary ocular adjustments of accommodation and convergence. Some form of an image or object must be used in order that fixation, necessary to accommodation, may take place; yet this object must not change in size, clearness, detail, or any of a number of other ways that visual cues might result; and the possibilities of double images must be eliminated.

The degree to which apparatus designed to fit the above requirements has succeeded is a question of individual evaluation; a comprehensive survey, including illustrations of apparatus, is given by Woodworth (3, pp. 665-680). Earliest efforts employed hanging threads, one of which was moved toward and away from the observer in order to isolate accommodation. This was criticized as not eliminating convergence or visual cues, such as detail and a double image. The use of a straight-edge movable in distance from an observer is more conclusive than the thread but may permit visual cues. It also presents a difficult object upon which to focus. Later studies employed circles of light as the object, with control of retinal image size achieved by variation of the diameter of the spot. Results from this apparatus indicate some possibility that unknown "competing" cues are present in the situation.

Several attacks upon the problem have been made with modified stereoscopes. The earliest of these employed mirrors, telescoping sighting tubes for adjusting the distance of a milk glass "object," and an aperture of standard size and position in the tubes for maintaining constant retinal image size. The main criticism against the use of this apparatus is that, if the milk glass is completely without texture, it presents no object for fixation; whereas, if it does have detail, the texture will provide visual cues. A later modification (23) used a binocular means for controlling the size of the retinal image from numbers from a standard acuity test. Efforts to isolate convergence rather than accommodation have had similar difficulties in eliminating visual cues.

AUDITORY SPACE

Since the localization of sounds in space depends primarily upon the relative stimulation of the two ears, apparatus for investigation of necessary conditions has as its chief requirement a method for administering sound stimuli to the two ears under controlled conditions. The simplest instrument for the purpose is the *sound cage* or auditory perimeter, which may consist of a metal circle, hemisphere, sphere, or rotary arc within which the subject sits. A source of sound, such as an earphone, is moved to various positions with reference to the location of the subject within the device, permitting auditory stimulation from any angle. The main difficulty of this apparatus for precise studies is its lack of provision for controlling extraneous noises and reflections of the stimulus sound.

This weakness is overcome by the use of a system of stimulation whereby each ear receives an independent stimulus through a transmission device such as an earphone fitted to the ear. The relations being studied (intensity, time, and phase) are controlled electrically (by attenuators, switching arrangements, and impedance networks). Other investigations have provided stimulation from microphones located as ears on a "wax man" which pick up sounds in the environment of the dummy and deliver them through earphones to corresponding ears of a subject located in another environment. Similar combinations of several microphones and loudspeakers have been employed in transmitting a stereophonic effect with, for example, a symphony. It is of interest to compare these procedures with earlier efforts for controlling the stimulus to the individual ears by means of sound tubes, a well-known example of which, the *pseudophone*, was used for reversing the stimuli.

PERCEPTION OF MOVEMENT

Visual stimulus movement.—Apparatus for the study of
the conditions for perception of a moving visual stimulus is
typified by that of Brown (24). It consists of an endless band
of white paper which passes behind an aperture in a light-tight
box at a controlled rate of speed, and on which are pasted black
figures. It is possible to vary the speed of the moving stimulus,
the size of the field through which the stimulus moves, the illumination of the field, the size and form of the objects, the
number of objects in the field, and the distance of the objects
from the observer. In addition, adjustment can be made for
monocular or binocular viewing and, by means of reduction
screens, for the elimination of some undesirable cues. A com-

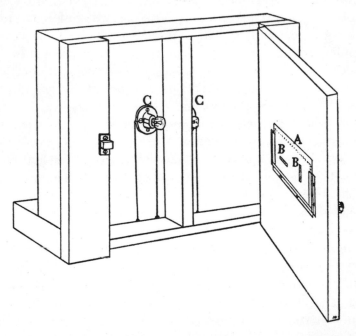

Fig. 7 - 12—Phi phenomenon apparatus. (From
Seward [25] courtesy of the author and the *American journal of psychology*)

parison apparatus is used to permit phenomenal matching with a standard stimulus situation.

Apparent movement.—Investigations of the perception of movement in the absence of physical movement employ situations in which successive stimulation of the eye is made by still objects which may be varied from one another in intensity and in separation distance, and for which the time interval between stimulations may be controlled. In other instances, slightly different pictures are presented in rapid succession, employing the situation typical of the motion pictures.

The most frequently used laboratory device for demonstrating apparent movement and its conditions is the *phi phenomenon apparatus,* many inexpensive forms of which have been suggested in the literature. One of these is illustrated in Figure 7 - 12. A light-tight box is divided by a partition, and a light source operated from a separate circuit is provided for each side. An aperture is cut in the front side of the box and is fitted with a rack for holding an opaque card in which are cut circles, bars, or other stimulus forms. When, for example, each side of the partition is equipped with a bar stimulus, as shown, and a time-control switching device is used to light first one chamber and then the other, the bar appears to move from the first to the second position. By changing the time between the stimuli, one may cause them to appear to be on simultaneously, successively, or to move from one to the other. Distance is altered by inserting different slides in the aperture, and intensity is controlled by means of rheostats in the light-source circuits.

Another arrangement, permitting a comparison of real and apparent movement, employs a similar light box with an opal glass front behind which are located a movable slide (on the top half) and a set of stationary stimuli for apparent movement (on the bottom half). Another utilizes three horizontal light boxes (movable and provided with apertures) and a circular, hand-operated switch to control exposure; a modification of this with several light boxes arranged in a circle has been used to demonstrate rotary phi phenomena. Still others suggest shadow casting, Lissajou figures, flashlights, and many other arrangements.

The above are primarily demonstrational devices. For purposes of research on apparent movement, modifications of the Dodge tachistoscope have been used. Since this instrument provides control over two (or more) stimulus fields which may be presented successively (or simultaneously) to one or both eyes, it is ideally suited for the study of the phenomenon. For a description of this apparatus see the earlier section on visual exposure control.

PERCEPTUAL CONSTANCY

The fact that the perception of objects does not correspond to the specific retinal image of the stimulus, but is influenced by the subject's knowledge of the object, has led to the use of combinations of apparatus, the chief requirements of which are careful control of the perceptual field of the observer. Experimentally produced variation is introduced to determine the effects of such cues as illumination and diversity of field upon the perception of color, size, and form of objects.

Apparatus utilized in the study of color constancy includes methods for controlling illumination (episcotisters, absorption media, changes in angle of incidence), for suggesting illumination (shadow casters, projectors), and for reducing the number of cues present to observers by concealing the surroundings of a given stimulus (reduction or hole screens). A setup of this type (26) is illustrated in Figure 7 - 13; a comprehensive survey, including numerous illustrations is given by Woodworth (3).

ILLUSION APPARATUS

The use of apparatus for verifying visual illusions is common in laboratory courses. The most popular illusion for the purpose is probably the Muller-Lyer, and many different instruments have been devised to permit objective measurement of

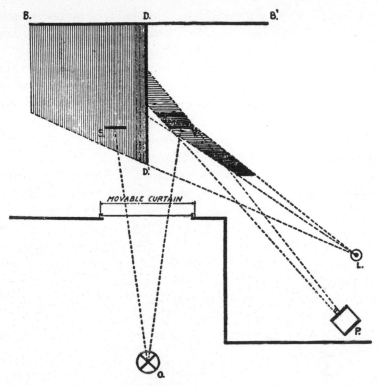

Fig. 7 - 13—Arrangement for studying color constancy. Observer (O) perceives a limited field divided by partition (DD') and backed by background (BB'). General illumination is provided by lamp (L) and concentrated or focused light by a concealed lantern (P). Stimulus (S) falls in the shadow of the partition while stimulus (V) also shielded from L receives light from P. The field may be diversified by introducing other disks. (From Henneman [26] courtesy of the *Archives of psychology* and the American Psychological Association)

the extent of illusion. All have in common the provision for measurement of standard and variable stimulus lengths and for adjustment, by the subject or the experimenter, of the length of one stimulus. The general procedure consists of setting the adjustable stimulus so that it is judged perceptually equal in length to the standard and measuring the discrepancy in lengths by means of linear scales on the apparatus.

Another illusion for which apparatus may be constructed readily is the Zollner, in which short diagonals appear to displace the line through which they are drawn. A device may be constructed so that the angle between two horizontal lines may be adjusted until the lines are judged parallel by the subject, and so that the actual angle is indicated by a scale on the back of the apparatus.

Drawings of these two types of apparatus are given in Figure 7 - 14. Adjustment of the card on which the lines of Muller-Lyer form are drawn is accomplished by sliding the wooden bar to which it is attached. The angle of the horizontal lines

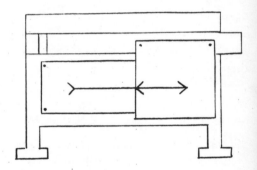

Fig. 7 - 14—Illusion apparatus: (above) Muller-Lyer, (below) Zollner

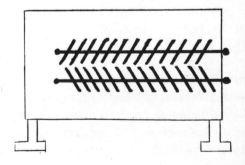

in the Zollner device is adjusted by means of a worm gear and lever arrangement behind the screen which increases or decreases the distance between the lines at one end—the other end of each being fixed.

Eye Movements in Reading

The study of movements of the eyes during reading tasks has contributed much to the understanding of the perceptual reading process; and apparatus for the observation and recording of these movements has progressed from simple observational schemes to highly standardized and commercially produced instruments. Earliest methods employed a mirror placed so that an observer could watch the eye movements from a position behind the reader. An example of this type of arrangement consisted of a headgear band on which a mirror is mounted. In other instances, a peep hole in the center of the copy being read furnished a means of observation; or a telescope permitted direct observation from a distance.

A contact microphone attached to the eye has been used to indicate the number of movements, as has also a similar pneumatic form of pickup device. Many earlier recorders employed objects attached directly to the eye. These included small cups with projecting recording styli, and similar cups with threads which operated external levers. Others had plates attached to the cornea support a mirror from which light was reflected to a photographic film; or a mirror was attached to the closed lid of one eye while the subject read with the other eye. For a review of these early methods of recording eye movements, see Tinker (27).

The method which has come into most general use consists essentially of the photographing of a beam of light reflected directly from the cornea. Instruments of this type are termed *ophthalmographs,* and are manufactured commercially for clinical and educational use. The basic operation of an ophthalmograph may be seen from the drawing in Figure 7 - 15. Light from the lamp (2) strikes the cornea of the subject's eye and

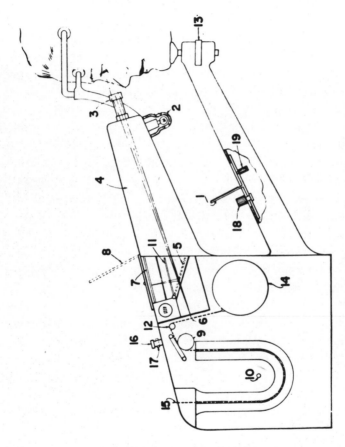

Fig. 7-15—Diagram of an ophthalmograph
(Courtesy American Optical Co.)

reflects into the lens tube (3). Here it is focussed and projected on the moving film (6) which is driven from a supply roll (14) by a drive roller (9) through a combination developer-fixer tank (10) and out a slot (15) ready to be viewed. Initial centering and focussing of the light rays is accomplished by means of a movable mirror (5) which may be dropped into the path of the rays from the lens to reflect the beam to a viewing screen (7). Many auxiliary features are available on these instruments—such as provision for control of illumination of reading material and for photographing identification data on the record.

Other recent techniques for recording eye movements have measured electrical potentials at or near the eye during reading. In one of these the corneo-retinal potential is recorded, for the change in that potential has been shown to be proportionate to the sine of the angle of rotation of the eye. Another procedure infers eye movements from action potential records from the extrinsic eye muscles. In comparing these techniques to that of corneal reflection as employed in the typical ophthalmograph, one reviewer (27) concludes in favor of corneal reflection procedures for general use.

OTHER PERCEPTUAL APPARATUS

Because the study of perceptual phenomena is linked so closely with study of the senses, a major portion of perceptual equipment is that already considered in discussions of vision, audition, and other senses. The chief need for instruments in each case is in the control and quantification of the physical stimulus. From the discussion of vision, relevant devices include photometers, episcotisters, monochromators, filters, color mixers, and measures of acuity and color vision; and those in audition include oscillators, filters, attenuators, wave analyzers, and sound recorders. Tachistoscopes and similar instruments for visual exposure control are considered in an earlier section.

REFERENCES

1. PYLE, W. H. *Laboratory manual in the psychology of learning.* Baltimore: Warwick York, Inc., 1923.
2. MACPHEE, H. M. A simple inexpensive exposure apparatus, *Amer. j. psychol.,* 1942, 55, 419-421.
3. WOODWORTH, R. S. *Experimental psychology.* New York: Henry Holt and Co., 1938.
4. RAY, W. S. A memory drum for paired associates learning, *J. gen. psychol.,* 1946, 34, 239-242.
5. BUEL, J. An electrically controlled film slide projector, *J. exp. psychol.,* 1938, 23, 661-664.
6. GULLIKSEN, H. A new form of tachistoscope, *J. gen. psychol.,* 1932, 6, 223-226. Also CHOU, S. K. An automatic card feeder and catcher mechanism, *J. gen. psychol.,* 1930, 3, 179-182.
7. HILGARD, E. R. Methods and procedures in the study of learning. Chapt. 15, in STEVENS, S. S. (ed.) *Handbook of experimental psychology.* New York: John Wiley Sons, Inc., 1951.
8. McGEOCH, J. A., and IRION, A. L. *The psychology of human learning.* New York: Longmans, Green and Co., 1952.
9. UNDERWOOD, B. J. *Experimental psychology.* New York: Appleton-Century-Crofts, Inc., 1949.
10. GURNEE, H. A portable bolthead maze, *Amer. j. psychol.,* 1928, 51, 405-406.
11. BOUSFIELD, W. A., and NOWLES, B. The construction of a punch maze, *J. exp. psychol.,* 1945, 35, 330-333.
12. MELTON, A. W. (ed.) *Apparatus tests.* Washington, D. C.: U. S. Govt. Printing Office, 1947. (AAF Aviation Psychol. Prog. Research Report No. 4.)
13. RUGER, H. A. The psychology of efficiency: An experimental study of the processes involved in the solution of mechanical puzzles and in the acquisition of skill in their manipulation. *Arch. psychol. N. Y.,* 1910, vol. 2, no. 15.
14. FREEMAN, F. N. *Experimental education.* Boston: Houghton Mifflin Co., 1916.
15. HANFMANN, E., and KASANIN, J. A method for the study of concept formation. *J. psychol.,* 1937, 3, 521-540.
16. MAIER, N. R. F. Reasoning in humans. I. On direction, *J. comp. psychol.,* 1930, 10, 115-144.
17. YERKES, R. M. New method for studying ideational behavior, *J. comp. psychol.,* 1921, 1, 369-394.
18. WELFORD, A. T. An apparatus for use in studying serial performance, *Amer. j. psychol.,* 1952, 65, 91-97.
19. HILGARD, E. R., and MARQUIS, D. G. *Conditioning and learning.* New York: D. Appleton Century Co., 1940.
20. SCHLOSBERG, H., and CARMICHAEL, L. A simple apparatus for the conditioned reflex, *Amer. j. psychol.,* 1931, 43, 120-122.
21. FOLEY, J. P. A classroom demonstration of the conditioned response, *Amer. j. psychol.,* 1941, 54, 418-422.
22. CARR, H. A. *An introduction to space perception.* New York: Longmans, Green Co., 1935.

23. GRANT, V. W. Accommodation and convergence in visual space perception, *J. exp. psychol.*, 1942, 31, 89-104.
24. BROWN, J. F. The visual perception of velocity, *Psychol. Forsch.*, 1931, 14, 199-232.
25. SEWARD, G. H. A device for demonstrating apparent visual motion, *Amer. j. psychol.*, 1932, 44, 348-349.
26. HENNEMAN, R. H. A photometric study of the perception of object color, *Arch. psychol.*, 1935, no. 179, p. 88.
27. TINKER, M. A. Eye movements in reading, *J. educ. res.*, 1936, 30, 241-277. Also *Psychol. bull.*, 1946, 43, 93-120.
28. ITTELSON, W. H. *The Ames demonstrations in perception.* Princeton: Princeton University Press, 1952.

CHAPTER 8

Bioelectricity

Fruitful inferences about the nature of behavior and the responsiveness of living material have resulted from the observation of electrical properties of organic matter. With respect to the human body it is common knowledge that patterns of electric potentials taken from the scalp are a diagnostic aid in detecting neural pathology; that action potentials taken from various parts of the body have been used as a basis for such concepts as "implicit speech" and "ideomotor action"; and that skin resistance phenomena are in some way tied up with the emotions.

It is not the purpose of this section to review the psychological significance of bioelectric variables or to review any of the conclusions which can be made therefrom. Instead, the problems of technique and instrumentation in this area are discussed to provide a broader basis for psychological use and evaluation of these electrical variables. The material which follows is divided into sections on (1) the general nature of bioelectric potentials, (2) specific electrical manifestations, and (3) the technical problems which arise in their measurement.

THE GENERAL NATURE OF BIOELECTRICITY

Just how electrical properties of organic tissue are produced is not a question on which there is currently complete agreement. On the laboratory facts, however, there is no essential disagreement, for many electrical phenomena can be reliably demonstrated. For example, two electrodes placed at any two points separated on the surface of the human body will show a measurable difference in electrical potential. With appropriate instruments a potential difference can be shown between the inside and outside of an axon. And it can be conclusively shown that the conduction of a nerve impulse along a nerve fiber is accompanied by a potential difference extending longitudinally along the fiber. To explain these electrical phenomena several theories have been proposed, a few of which will be noted here.

One point of view holds that the smallest particles of organic tissue are bipolar molecules, electrically positive on one end and negative on the other. This presupposes a certain spatial arrangement and separation of the molecules and nonelectrical forces (structural and mechanical) which maintain electric fields by separating and aligning the charged molecules. An example of this situation would exist within the single cell where the cell membrane serves to separate charges within and without the cell with the result that the cell becomes polarized from the inside to the outside.

Another theory emphasizes the selective permeability of ions. According to this point of view certain membranes possess a differential permeability to positive and negative ions. Conduction is made possible by changes in relative permeability of the tissue membranes involved. At any given instant living tissue is made up of ion-permeable (or conducting) areas and ion-nonpermeable areas which are polarized by the accumulation of electric charges, much as in the case of an electrolytic condenser.

Still another explanation emphasizes electrochemistry and concludes that electrical phenomena within the body are produced in much the same way as the potential is produced in a voltaic cell. Here the critical components are the tissue membranes and the aqueous solutions in the surrounding cells, and the major factors in conduction are fluid concentrations and membrane penetration. Each electromotive force in tissue is considered as composed of a multitude of single potential differences located wherever differentiated structures come in contact. These forces remain in balance wherever possible, and, if tissue is injured, a current of imbalance flows. Diffusion forces between aqueous solutions and water-immiscible fluids contribute to concentration changes.

The differences between these and other points of view are small and of primary interest to the physiologist (1). Brief mention of them is made here, however, because of the implications they have for making electrical measurements on the body. There are important differences between measurements made from a dry cell or metallic conductor and those made from organic tissue. The magnitudes of electromotive forces emanating from the body are small and the internal resistance of the tissue is high, resulting in very low measurement currents. The chemical origin of these electrical properties dictates the importance of care and precaution in preventing disturbances created through the use of metallic wires (or electrolytic solutions) to connect the tissue to the measuring instruments. These and related problems will need to be treated in detail later.

SPECIFIC ELECTRICAL MANIFESTATIONS

Nerve Impulse

It is a primary characteristic of neural tissue that excitation by a stimulus at one locus in the cell is transmitted rapidly to other parts. This conduction, which usually proceeds from dendrites through the cell body and along the axon, is manifested by an electrical potential difference progressing longitudinally along the fiber. The amplitude of the change ranges from a few microvolts to the order of millivolts depending upon the animal and the nerve. The period is rapid, requiring measurement in milliseconds where accurate identification of components of the wave is desired.

There are two common ways to observe this transient potential. One places a reference electrode over inactive tissue (a killed end of the nerve) and the other electrode on the active nerve. This registers the sequence of changes under the "live" electrode (2, p. 55). A second method places both electrodes over live tissue and registers the diphasic potential change as the wave of activity passes from one electrode to the other (3, p. 13) (see Fig. 8 - 1).

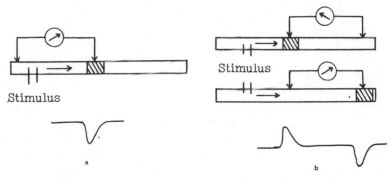

Fig. 8 - 1—Comparison of monophasic (a) and diphasic (b) recording of the nerve impulse

Nerve action potentials differ with the type of fiber, its size, momentary state, and the amount of compounding involved. Large fibers in mammalian nerves typically have three components: a spike, a negative after potential, and a positive after potential. The larger fibers have a more rapid rate of conduction and a larger spike potential than the smaller fibers. Spike duration, magnitude and duration of after potentials, as well as refractory periods, also vary with fiber size. For detailed descriptions of wave forms and electrical properties of nerves, see Erlanger and Gasser (4), Brink (2), and Brazier (3).

Muscle Action Potentials

When individual muscles contract, they exhibit a potential change like that of the nerve fiber. The predominate characteristic of the potential is its spike of relatively short duration (in the order of a millisecond) and the fact that the discharge repeats at a fairly high frequency (hundreds per second). The magnitudes of the potential change are fairly large, typical values ranging from 1 to 3 millivolts for heart contractions, and from about 50 microvolts to as much as 10 millivolts for skeletal muscle.

Several introductory characteristics are of importance in differentiating among uses of action potentials. For one thing, the response of muscle groups is of a magnitude which can be observed by placing pickup electrodes on the surface of the body over the muscle in question. This is of considerable importance, since the psychologist is more interested in responses of the intact human organism than he is in those of special muscle preparations.

Secondly, because the response observed is from a group of muscle fibers rather than an isolated one, the total potential change involves a mixture of frequencies. This gives the phenomenon a frequency characteristic which resembles "noise." Finally, there is little interest in the analysis of individual wave forms—such as exists for nerve impulses. Instead researchers more frequently are interested in total muscular output per unit of time. This creates specialized instrument needs for summating action potentials and registering total or average output rather than transient potentials.

ELECTRICAL POTENTIALS FROM SENSE ORGANS

It is a demonstrated property of sensory cells that they exhibit electrical changes when excited by adequate stimuli, and it is probably this electric change which initiates the sensory nerve impulse. In studying sensory phenomena, then, the role of the sense cells can be likened to photoelectric, mechanoelectric, chemoelectric, or thermoelectric transducers. In some instances the potential responses have been shown to be specific to certain stimuli (as in the case of taste); in others there are spatial temporal patterns of excitation (as in smell) (5).

The electrical sense responses which have been most widely studied are those of the eye and ear. The common practice is to place an "active" electrode over or in the receptor cells or the sensory nerve and a reference electrode over an inactive region. A potential difference is recorded which varies with the placement of the active electrode. If the electrodes are on the front and back of the eyeball, the resulting record is termed an *electroretinogram* (6). A comparable record for the ear is the *cochlear microphonic* or cochlear potential (7).

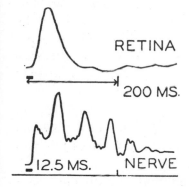

Fig. 8 - 2—Sensory potentials at the receptor and the sensory nerve for the eye. (By permission from *Vision*, by Bartley, 1941, D. Van Nostrand Co., Inc.)

In the development of theory the differentiation between potentials originating in the sense end organs and those involving action potentials of sensory nerves has been of major importance. A comparison of the optic-nerve discharge and the electroretinogram from the same short flash of light is shown in Figure 8 - 2. Oscillograph tracing of cochlear microphonics and action potentials from the midbrain are shown in Figure

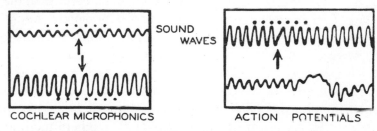

Fig. 8 - 3—Sensory potentials at the receptor and in the sensory nerve for the ear. (From Stevens and Davis [7] after Hallpike, Hartridge, and Rawdon Smith, *Proc. Roy. Soc.*, London, 1937, 122B, 175-185; courtesy The Royal Society)

8 - 3. The arrow indicates a point at which the phase of the sound waves was shifted 180 degrees.

ELECTRICAL ACTIVITY OF THE CORTEX

The popular term "brain waves" refers to the fluctuations in spontaneous electrical potential between two electrodes placed adjacent to the cerebral cortex, or between one such cortically located electrode and a second reference electrode placed in a "neutral" position, such as the lobe of the ear. These potentials are most frequently picked up from small electrodes attached to the scalp, although in connection with surgical techniques electrodes are sometimes placed in direct contact with the brain surface or, through the use of depth electrodes, with various brain levels.

The class name for instruments designed to record cortical potentials is *electroencephalograph,* and the process is *electroencephalography* when pickup is from the scalp or *electrocorticography* when pickup is from the cortex itself. Most instruments are designed with many channels to permit simultaneous recording from several locations and both hemispheres.

Potentials involved are characterized by a low magnitude (the order of microvolts) and a low frequency range (most fall below 30 cycles per second). It is somewhat common to refer to the magnitudes as low if less than 20 microvolts, average if from 20 to 50 microvolts, and high if above 50 microvolts. As can be noted in Figure 8 - 4, the potentials show a frequency pattern with characteristic peaks. These have been used as a basis for labeling or classifying the waves. One such classification employs the following breakdown (9).

1. *Alpha* waves, with frequency range from 8 to 13 cycles per second and an average of about 10 cps. The magnitude ranges from less than 5 microvolts to as much as 100 microvolts with most waves falling between 20 and 50 microvolts.

2. *Beta* waves, with frequency range from 13 to 30 cycles per second with an average of about 25. The magnitude ranges from about 3 to 20 microvolts.

3. *Gamma* waves, with a frequency range from 30 to 50 or more cycles per second, and a magnitude generally less than 10 microvolts.

4. *Delta* waves, with frequencies from 1 to 7 cps, and amplitudes as high as 200 to 500 microvolts, but generally around 100 microvolts.

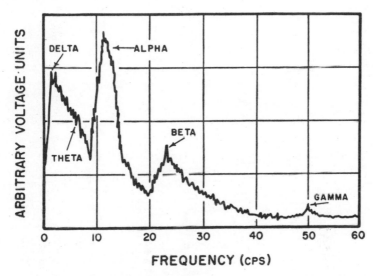

Fig. 8 - 4—The frequency spectrum of brain waves. (By permission from *Physiological psychology*, by Morgan and Stellar, 1950, McGraw-Hill Book Co., Inc.)

These exceedingly small potentials with low frequency rates suggest that instruments for their measurement must provide high amplification (gains in the order of millions) with a minimum of noise and with special attention paid to accurate amplification of low frequencies. Most of these problems will be considered individually later. A range of typical *electroencephalograms* (EEGs) is shown in Figure 8 - 5. They include (I) large and slow, 4 to 7 cps, waves common in young children; (II) alpha waves; (III) spindle waves observed while the subject is sleeping; (IV) rapid rhythms of between 20 and 24 cps.;

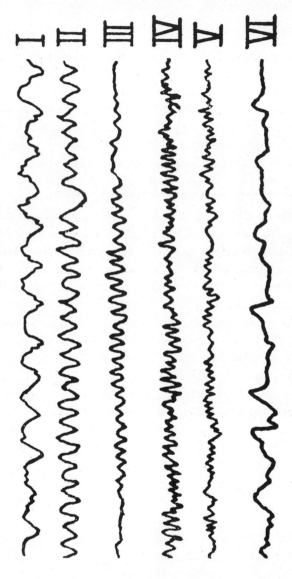

Fig. 8 - 5—Typical electroencephalograms. (From Loomis, Harvey, and Hobart [10] courtesy of the *Journal of experimental psychology* and the American Psychological Association)

(V) beta waves; (VI) large "random" waves characteristic of sound sleep.

ELECTRODERMAL PHENOMENA

It is common practice to divide electrical skin effects into two classes depending upon the operations by which they are observed. In one class of measurement an electric current is passed between two points on the skin and a determination of resistance, impedance, or conductance between the two locations is made. Such observations are termed *exodermal,* and, when the reference is change in resistance, etc., the term Fere phenomenon is frequently used (naming it after its discoverer) (11, 12). The second, or *endodermal,* class involves the measurement of the potential difference between two locations on the body. The change in this potential which accompanies adequate stimulation is often called the Tarchanoff phenomenon —also after its founder. When changes are referred to, the more general terms of *galvanic skin response* (GSR), *psychogalvanic reflex* (PGR), or *electrodermal response* are used.

When the exodermal characteristics are measured by passing a direct current between two electrodes on the skin, the "base" resistance may vary from less than 5,000 ohms to more than 100,000 ohms, depending upon numerous physical factors (such as the type, placement, size, and pressure of the pickup electrodes) and the amount of current passed through the subject—all in addition to the individual skin characteristics of the subjects. The magnitude of resistance change which occurs on stimulation is also determined by numerous variables. When the GSR is expressed in ohms resistance change, values range from 0 to over 20,000 ohms with most values falling below 5,000 ohms.

With alternating current, both the base impedance and the change in impedance on stimulation are found to be smaller than comparable DC measurements. This suggests that much of what is measured as "resistance" contains reactance components, particularly capacitive reactance. The presence of an

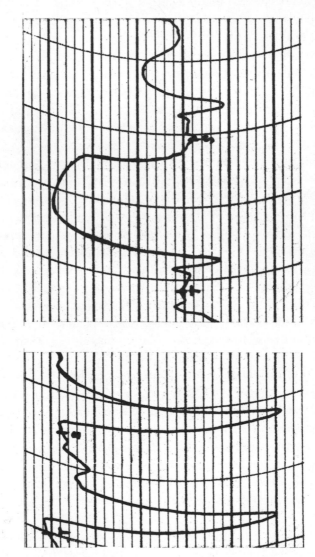

Fig. 8 · 6—Comparison of resistance (left) and potential (right) galvanic skin responses. Stimuli were introduced at points S and T. Units are not comparable.

appreciable capacity causes AC impedance of the skin to vary inversely with frequency of the current used. Changes in capacity and impedance upon stimulation are also a function of frequency and reach a practical limit for measurement purposes above 10,000 or 15,000 cycles per second.

The polarization capacity of the body, discussed above, is probably the basis for observed potential differences between various locations on the body and the changes in these potentials which are referred to as endodermal galvanic skin responses. As would be expected these potentials depend greatly upon the size and electrolytic properties of the electrodes used and vary markedly with electrode placement. Some workers employ a buccal electrode as a reference, others place both electrodes on the surface of the skin (or in an electrolyte which makes contact with the skin). The electrical wave form of potential change on stimulation is somewhat different from that of DC resistance change (see Fig. 8 - 6). It contains a brief and small change in one direction followed by a major change in the opposite direction. For a more detailed discussion of basic skin electricity, including such matters as equivalent resistance, current and frequency effects, and electrode placement differences, see reference 13.

In all of the above skin phenomena the changes which occur upon stimulation have a characteristic latency and period which influences instrumentation requirements. After the stimulus has been presented, the response does not occur for 1 to 3 or more seconds, and the return to a starting point is very slow (in the order of seconds). This complicates the amplification of changes for recording purposes.

ELECTRODES

The pickup devices in any bioelectric system play a crucial role, for it is necessary to bridge the gap between the observed organism and the measuring instrument with the least possible effect upon the properties being picked up or the system being observed. The problem is complicated by the fact that the pickup junction involves quite dissimilar substances; on the side of the instrument, metallic conductors; and for the organism, organic tissue with significant aqueous and electrolytic components.

If the metallic conductor is simply laid adjacent to the tissue, an interaction of the two in the form of ionic polarization within the electrolyte may take place, or a chemical reaction between the metal and the electrolyte may occur. If a potential difference is impressed between two such electrodes on tissue (as in measuring skin resistance or applying an electric stimulus), a current will flow and the process of electrode polarization will be intensified. When a current passes through an electrolyte, conduction is made possible by the movement of charged ions to their respective poles, and a consequent change in "apparent resistance" or voltage across the electrode junction appears. In addition, intersurface potentials, or "battery effects," build up as products of electrolysis and accumulate at the poles of the electrodes.

The conventional method of attacking these problems is to use a special boundary or junction between the tissue and the amplifier input. Where polarization is likely to be a problem, as in instances where direct current is involved, an effort is made to devise a nonpolarizing electrode—a goal which is never completely achieved. Fortunately, where alternating potentials are involved the bidirectional aspect of the phenomenon tends to cancel out polarization effects and removes the need for nonpolarizing electrodes. Instances in which polarization is a major problem include the measurement of skin resistance and the application of a direct or monophasic pulsating current to tissue.

Minimum polarization is usually achieved by using a junction of metal with one of its salts which then makes an electrolytic junction with the tissue and its saline solution. The most common metals and salts for this purpose are zinc-zinc sulphate, mercury-mercuric sulphate, and silver-silver chloride.

Because the first two involve ions injurious to tissue, their action needs to be contained and isolated from the tissue. This may be done with porous clay, blotting paper, and similar porous substances, which may be soaked in the salt, laid adjacent to the metal, and isolated from the tissue by gauze or electrode jelly.

Of the above, the most universally applicable is silver-silver chloride; for it avoids the dissimilar salt junction of the other two and is convenient to use. The chloride of silver is insoluble, and as silver ions unite with free chloride ions from the tissue, they deposit as silver chloride on the surface of the electrode. The electrodes are commonly made by coating silver (wire, disk, or plate) by placing it at the positive pole of a low-voltage (about 3 volts) saline electrolytic bath until a slight graying, due to the deposit of silver chloride, appears (19, p. 57).

Silver-silver chloride electrodes can be used in most situations, although for various reasons workers use alternate techniques. For example, Gibbs and Gibbs (14), while stating that silver is very satisfactory for electroencephalography, recommend (for economy and convenience) the use of virgin solder with a composition of 60 per cent or more tin and 40 per cent or less lead. When microelectrodes are needed, the use of steel is often recommended over silver because of unusual strength requirements. A very wide range of metals has been used in one situation or another. Liquid electrodes are common. One of these involves immersion of the tissue in an electrolytic bath; another is a micropipette made of glass and filled with saline. For recording the electroretinogram, one electrode is frequently imbedded in a contact lens making liquid junction with the cornea.

Earliest work with brain potentials employed needle electrodes inserted into the cortical tissue. Later work with humans has generally employed small electrodes placed on the surface of the scalp. The most common type consists either of a flat drop of solder or a small metal cup from which fine gauge enameled

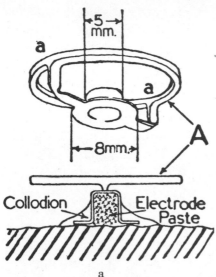

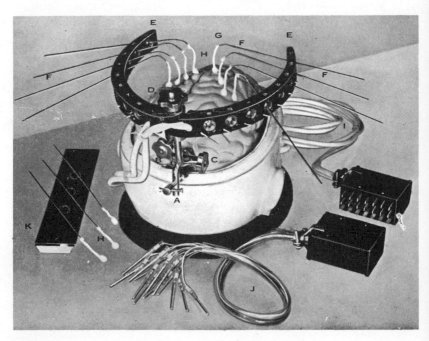

Fig. 8-7—Electrodes for electroencephalography. (a) Cup type, filled with electrode paste and held to scalp with collodion. (b) Cortical electrode holder for wick-type electrodes. Each electrode rod (F) terminates in a flexible silver wire (G) to which the wick electrodes (H) are attached. The wicks are kept saturated with saline. ([a] From Hill and Parr [19] after Greville and St. John-Loe, courtesy MacDonald and Co., Ltd., London. [b] Courtesy Grass Instrument Co., Quincy, Mass.)

a

b

wire leads through a shielded cable to the amplifier (Fig. 8 - 7). The electrode is about five millimeters in diameter and about two millimeters thick. When the electrode is applied, the hair is parted to expose as much of the scalp as possible, and the electrode is fastened in place by a film of collodion applied with a medicine dropper and dried with a blast of air. The electrode is removed with acetone or alcohol. Contact between the electrode and the scalp is made with electrode jelly. For work with animals, or in conjunction with human surgery, special electrodes are often employed in direct contact with the cortex. They may consist of needle electrodes, small metal pellets, or electrolytic wick devices (Fig. 8 - 7).

In the study of muscle behavior, fine needle electrodes are sometimes employed, being inserted deep into the center of the muscle. One method for constructing these is to pass a fine varnished wire through a hypodermic needle. Often, electrodes consisting of metal plates are applied to the exterior surface of the body, one over the muscle and the other over a neutral area. Contact is made by gauze which has been soaked in saline solution, or directly by means of electrode paste. The latter technique is used extensively in electrocardiography.

Devices for attaching electrodes to the skin for electrodermal measurement are various. Some workers use finger tip liquid immersion electrodes controlling area by taping the fingers. Others endeavor to keep the moisture level, contact area, and contact pressure constant by covering a zinc plate with a paste of saturated zinc sulphate kaolin over which a layer of cotton soaked in saline solution is placed. This cotton communicates by means of a wick with reservoirs of saline solution. Pressure is controlled by inflatable, manometrically regulated balloons surrounding the hand. Still another electrode is constructed in the form of a cup (Fig. 8 - 8). The metal (for example, zinc) is placed in the flat bottom of the plastic cup with a lead-in wire attached through the base; over the metal may be placed a layer of blotting paper soaked in zinc sulphate solution; the remainder of the cup is filled with sodium chloride base paste. The cup is held next to the skin by a bandage or soft rubber straps.

Electrode pastes or jellies of various compositions have been employed for bioelectric measurement. The most common are sodium chloride solutions with inert bases such as kaolin. Several of these are available commercially in medical supply houses under trade names. Some workers with EEG recommend

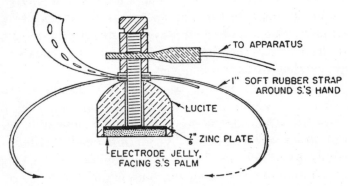

Fig. 8 - 8—Drawing of a GSR electrode. (From Haggard and Gerbrands [16] courtesy of the *Journal of experimental psychology* and the American Psychological Association)

a bentonite paste; with GSR some workers prefer zinc oxide over sodium chloride. A sodium chloride paste used for some time by the writer is made as follows: Solution 1 contains 50 g gum tragacanth ribbon, 60 g glycerine, 100 cc H_2O (warm). It is allowed to stand in a warm place for 12 hours. Solution 2 is 1000 cc saturated NaCl solution. Solution 3 contains 300 cc distilled H_2O and 20 g potassium bitartrate. Solution 3 is added to 2. This is then mixed with solution 1 and 3 g phenol added.

Several sources of error exist at any electrode junction. The most common of these are: drying of the tissue under the electrode, unsuspected leaks to ground, improper or insecure attachment resulting in electrode "noise," and shorted electrodes. The last mentioned most readily occurs because of an electrolytic film (perhaps of electrode paste) between the electrodes. This serves to shunt any high impedance input pickup.

GENERAL PROPERTIES OF AMPLIFIERS
FOR BIOLOGICAL RECORDING

There are typically three or four features of any biological amplifier which differentiate it from other amplifiers. An effort will be made to point these out here. Since it is assumed that most readers have not worked on amplifiers, the emphasis will be on the general descriptive language which might be referred to in commercial literature.

GAIN

The most obvious specification of an amplifier is how much it will amplify. This is its maximum gain which is most commonly expressed as the ratio of output voltage to input voltage. A simple voltage ratio is common although decibel expressions are also used. In determining the gain required for a given situation, one needs simply to determine the required output voltage to drive the registration device and divide this by the minimum potential being "picked up" or observed. For example, to record a brain-wave oscillation of one microvolt amplitude with an oscillograph requiring one volt to move it one centimeter, a gain of one million would be minimum satisfactory.

Expressions of gain generally reflect the purpose for which an amplifier is designed. A statement of voltage gain indicates the extent to which the instrument is a voltage amplifier, or is designed to increase a voltage. Pure voltage amplifiers operate at about the same current level throughout and may lack power to drive current consuming recording apparatus. Therefore, attention needs to be paid to power output characteristics as well. In high-gain amplification the preamplifier serves primarily as a voltage amplifier, and power is generated in the last or output stages of the main amplifier.

STAGES

The essence of vacuum-tube amplification is the valvelike action of the tube grid in producing a change in plate current to accompany a change in grid voltage. With an appropriate load in the plate circuit of the tube the change in voltage drop across the load is large in magnitude as compared to the change in voltage at the grid. The amount of such amplifying or stepping up which can be accomplished within a single tube or amplification unit is limited by physical factors. Amplifiers embody the extension of such amplification units, or stages, in the sense of leading one into another, each building up the output of the former.

Reference may be simply "three-stage amplifier," "four-stage amplifier," etc., although more specific designation is usual, such as "two stages of voltage preamplification leading into a three-stage main amplifier," or "three voltage amplification stages and one power stage." It will be noted that of the amplifiers illustrated below the first has three stages mounted as separate units, the second has a total of five stages, and the last one has three.

INPUT AND OUTPUT CHARACTERISTICS

The junctions which the amplifier makes at its input and output sides are very important to the quality of output received and the effects which the amplifier may have on the system being observed. As a class, biological amplifiers are designed to have high input impedance. This means that if the amplifier leads are connected directly to tissue, the equivalent of a very high resistance (order of megohms) has been placed across the tissue and an insignificant amount of current is drawn from the tissue. It is this feature which prevents current operated instruments, such as the galvanometer, from being very useful in directly measuring small voltages in a high-resistance circuit such as organic tissue.

The output characteristics of the amplifier need to be appropriate to the needs of the particular registration device. If a current-operated signal pen or oscillograph is to be operated, an appropriate power output must be generated. Several output characteristics may be relevant, such as output impedance (usually low), maximum output in either direction, and normal load resistance.

COUPLING

An important characteristic of any multiple-stage amplifier is the procedure employed for linking the output of one stage to the grid of the next. Such a junction of stages is termed a coupling. There are numerous coupling systems. A wire may lead directly from the plate of the first stage to the grid of the second stage, resulting in *direct* coupling; or the junction between the plate and grid may be across a condenser, resulting in *capacity* coupling. These two forms are most frequently employed in bioelectric measurement.

Coupling has a significant relationship to the frequency characteristic of the amplifier. If the potential change is slow, as is the case in the galvanic skin response, the resulting changes in the plate circuit will be slow. The passage of the potential change across the load resistor on to the next stage will be completely blocked by a coupling condenser. For this reason direct coupled amplifiers find extensive use in the measurement of the GSR. When high gain is needed, direct-coupled amplifiers present certain difficulties. With many stages of amplification the maintenance of correct biases on successive stages is difficult. There is a tendency for a cumulative drift to occur and for the circuits to be inherently unstable because of the complex relations which must be maintained between grid and cathode potentials. In spite of these difficulties direct coupling has its place in laboratory amplifiers whenever it becomes necessary to measure currents of low and zero frequency, and considerable progress has been made during the last decade in improving DC amplifier design.

When the rate of alternation is sufficiently high, as is the case with some brain and most muscle potentials, it is usually more convenient to employ capacity coupling. Here care must be exercised in the choice of components to prevent undue frequency discrimination. The coupling condenser prevents the amplification of direct-current changes, such as drift due to changes in the contact resistance at the electrodes, without necessarily interfering with the transmission of alternating currents. Of the illustrations in this chapter, it will be noted that Figures 8 - 10 and 8 - 11 are capacity coupled, whereas Figure 8 - 12 is direct coupled.

TUBE ARRANGEMENT

Another feature of importance in amplifying apparatus depends on whether each stage uses a single tube (or its equivalent) or consists of a symmetrical arrangement of two tubes. When a single set of tube elements (cathode, grid, plate) is involved, the stage is termed single sided; when two tubes are symmetrically arranged to operate on opposite halves of a cycle, the stage is termed push-pull. Single-sided arrangements have certain advantages for achieving maximum linearity at fairly low gains but are generally less efficient than push-pull arrangements. For this reason, the majority of biological amplifiers are push-pull.

The essential feature of the push-pull circuit is that each stage consists of two tubes operating in a symmetrical arrangement about common cathodes. They operate in class AB or B (see below) in such a way that they remain on the linear part of their characteristic while amplifying opposite directions of the input signal. That is, one tube conducts on positive fluctuations from the reference point while the other conducts on the negative portion of the cycle. In this manner the distortion introduced by one·tube is to a large degree cancelled out by that of its mate; and the total efficiency of each stage is about double that of a single tube because each tube is able to use its full linear response.

It is possible to so arrange a push-pull stage that outside

interferences, such as AC pickup in the input leads, is given very high negative feedback while out-of-phase (push-pull) signals receive no negative feedback.

This is usually accomplished by having any input signal with reference to ground impressed in phase on each tube of the pair so that the net output change at the tube plates is practically zero as the simultaneous change is impressed upon a common large cathode resistor. The term *discrimination ratio* is often used to describe the ratio of the output voltage change of a signal applied to both grids in opposite phase to the output voltage of a signal of the same magnitude applied to both grids in phase.

CLASS

Amplification units are frequently designated with a class letter which indicates the portion of the input cycle that plate current is expected to flow—which is determined by the grid voltage employed for static operation of the stage. For example, a class A amplifier is one in which the static bias potential is near the center of the linear portion of the characteristic curve and static plate current is about halfway between zero and maximum (Fig. 8-9). The grid bias and impressed signal voltages are arranged so that plate current flows continuously, cutoff values are never reached, and the grid never becomes positive. The chief advantage of this form of operation is that the tube may be made to operate on the linear portion of its characteristic curve during negative and positive signal swings with a minimum of distortion. The disadvantage is inefficiency, since the range of plate-current change is limited by the short portion of the curve within which the tube is operating. This type of amplifier, therefore, is most useful in situations where linearity is required and high efficiency is not essential.

A class B amplifier is one in which the static grid voltage is set at approximately the cutoff value so that plate current is about zero when no external voltage is impressed on the grid. This arrangement is such that the plate current flows about half

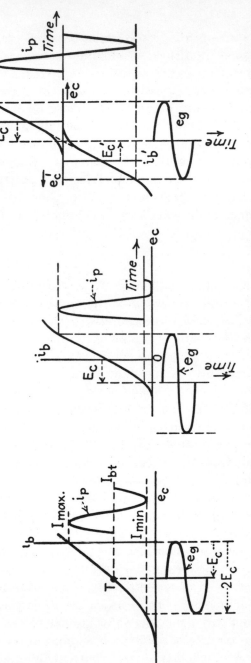

Fig. 8·9—Some classes of amplifier operation: (left) Class A; (center) Class B, two tubes in push-pull. Crucial factors are changes in plate current (i_p) as a function of changes in grid voltage (e_g), projected from the tube characteristic curves. (By permission from *Theory and application of electron tubes,* by Reich, 1939, McGraw-Hill Book Co., Inc.)

of each cycle when an alternating grid voltage is applied. Its major disadvantage is distortion when used in a single-sided arrangement, for the negative portion of cycles on the grid voltage will produce practically no change in plate current. Advantage occurs when two tubes are arranged in push-pull in such a way that one of the tubes is operating during the positive half cycles of the impressed wave while the other tube is operating during the negative swings. In this way the range of possible plate-current changes is approximately doubled.

Other arrangements include class AB in which grid voltages are arranged such that plate current flows for more than half but less than the entire cycle; and class C in which static grid voltage is below cutoff so that plate current flows for less than half of each cycle of incident voltage. For most biological amplifiers the class AB is used. Here the advantages discussed in A and B are both achieved to a large degree. The tubes are made to operate on the most linear part of the characteristic for linearity, and efficiency is kept high.

DISTORTION

The amplification problem in electrophysiology reduces to one of proper magnification of voltages and adequate registration of these amplified magnitudes. The chief criterion is sufficient amplitude with a minimum of distortion. If the amplifier is functioning properly, the output will be identical with the impressed potential in every way except magnitude. Any alteration in the form of the wave as it passes through the amplifier is distortion.

There are several major classes of distortion of concern here. One is *amplitude distortion,* or nonlinearity. This implies a nonlinear relationship between the plate current changes and the grid potential changes, which causes the output wave to be different in shape from the source voltage wave. It is determined by a large number of considerations, such as the linearity of the dynamic characteristic of the tubes used, the location of the static biases and feedback voltages, and the magnitude of input signal voltage swings as they relate to the previous factors. The simplest example is seen in "overloading" an amplifier by applying too large a signal voltage with the result that the input tubes are forced to operate beyond the linear portion of their characteristics.

A second class may be called *frequency discrimination* and occurs when an amplifier magnifies the voltages of some frequencies more than it does those of other frequencies, with the result that the relative amplitudes of components of a complex wave are altered. It arises from the fact that certain circuit impedances are a function of frequency. The frequency-response characteristics of commercial amplifiers are typically specified by the manufacturer in graphical form, or by a verbal statement, such as percentage or decibel variations through designated frequency changes.

Phase distortion occurs when the phase relationships within a wave are altered during the process of amplification.

NOISE

One might assume that by hooking successive amplification units or stages together there would be no limit to the amount of amplification that could be achieved. From a practical point of view this is definitely not true. Slight current and potential fluctuations (noise) in early stages of amplification get amplified along with the impressed voltages until, with high degrees of amplification, they achieve large enough proportions to obscure the record of the incident waves. When it is recalled that the gain of EEG amplifiers is over one million, it can be seen that an undesired circuit voltage fluctuation in the first stage of one millionth of a volt would enter the recording mechanism as a change of one volt.

Among the sources of noise which can be controlled is improper shielding of the subject and the equipment, in one case from stray external electrical fields (such as the 60-cycle fields which are present in most buildings) and in the second case in shielding each stage from each other and the power supply from the grids of the amplifier stages. Power-supply shifts, such as fluctuations in battery potential, and shifts in line voltage may create noise. Faulty insulation, poor connections, and vibrations are other preventable sources.

Electrical fluctuations in the vacuum tubes contribute noise. Special nonmicrophonic tubes for the reduction of such factors are manufactured and widely used. Tube noise may arise from small variations in filament or cathode emission, insecure mounting of parts, small interelectrode currents within the tube, and atmospheric ions left in the tube. Least reducible of all are fluctuations arising from the thermal movement of free electrons in resistors in early stages. These movements make minute potential changes which are amplified.

Noise characteristics of commercial amplifiers are expressed as maximum microvolts during a specified period of time. It is important to note whether a peak-to-peak or RMS measurement of no-signal response has been made.

TYPICAL AMPLIFIERS

Many of the above features of amplifiers can be seen by considering three instruments designed for different purposes. The first (Fig. 8 - 10) is a three-stage capacity-coupled high-gain amplifier for muscular-action potentials. The second (Fig. 8 - 11) is a five-stage capacity-coupled electroencephalograph amplifier. The third (Fig. 8 - 12) is a three-stage direct-coupled amplifier for measuring the galvanic skin response. All three operate in push-pull.

Note the use of large coupling condensers in Figures 8 - 10 and 8 - 11 and their absence in Figure 8 - 12. Frequency discrimination is intentionally introduced in Figure 8 - 11 by making the coupling between the third and fourth stages variable. High frequencies are filtered out by condensers across the input of the last stage. Each stage in Figure 8 - 10 is mounted on a separate removable can which plugs into a chassis containing basic supply circuits and interstage connections. Such

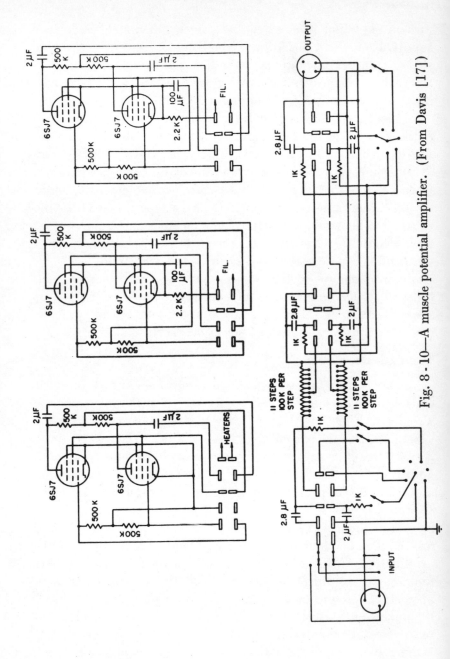

Fig. 8·10—A muscle potential amplifier. (From Davis [17])

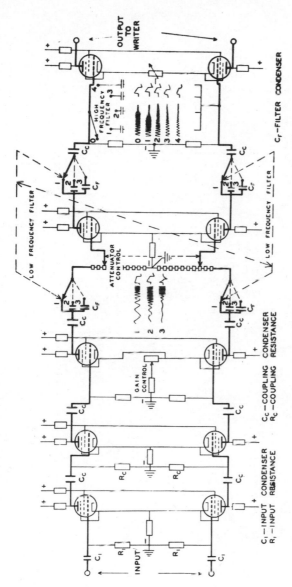

Fig. 8·11—An electroencephalograph amplifier. (By permission from *Clinical electroencephalography*, by Cohn, 1949, McGraw-Hill Book Co., Inc.)

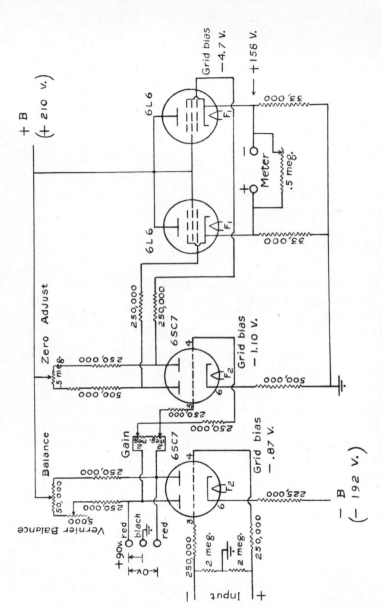

Fig. 8-12—An amplifier for the GSR. (From Trueblood and Grings [18] courtesy of The Journal Press, Provincetown, Mass.)

mounting has advantage in achieving shielding and in facilitating repair work.

Observe the various means for controlling amplifier gain. Figure 8 - 11 is provided with two, an attenuator across the input of stage four and a variable cathode potential on stage three. Figure 8 - 10 has a balance-step control at the input to stage two which functions in the same way as the continuous double potentiometer at the input of stage two in Figure 8 - 12. Discrete step input gain adjustments are much preferred to continuously variable controls in circumstances where rapid changes in gain are required, for the steps can be arranged to alter gain by a given factor each step. The most common practice is to provide an amplifier with two gain controls—one continuous for calibration purposes, the other discrete for making rapid operating changes. Or auxiliary devices may be used, as in the case of Figure 8 - 12 where the amplifier is driven by an input circuit equipped with an attenuator which has the effect of putting an attenuator at the amplifier input.

The methods for powering these amplifiers differ. In both of the first two the preamplifier stages are powered either by batteries or specially designed power supplies to reduce noise in the early stages of amplification. The high voltage for the following stages is provided by AC-operated supplies of a conventional sort, and DC filament supplies may be retained in these later stages to reduce hum. To operate most DC amplifiers, such as that in Figure 8 - 12, special power-supply requisites include voltage-stabilized supplies of both high positive and high negative voltages and a current-regulated filament supply.

AMPLIFIER CALIBRATION

The considerations of amplifier design are often of less importance to the psychologist than the problem of calibrating the equipment for a particular use or running tests to determine the general level of function of the instrument. This requires the introduction of a known potential at the input to the ampli-

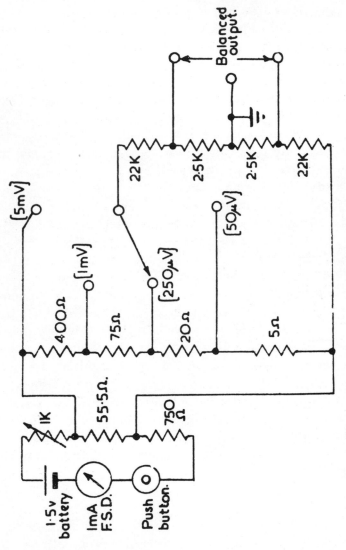

Fig. 8·13—A voltage calibrator circuit. (By permission from *Electrophysiological technique*, by C. J. Dickinson, 1950, Electronic Engineering, London)

fier so that the output of the various stages, or the amplifier as a whole, can be checked. It is therefore common practice to provide amplifiers with built-in voltage calibrators for convenience. For example, in the case of EEG amplifiers, the American Medical Association and the American Electroencephalographic Society, in specifying minimum requirements for electroencephalographs, both require built-in calibration devices. (For a full statement of these requirements see Gibbs and Gibbs, p. 126f.) A typical arrangement for supplying calibration voltages is shown in Figure 8 - 13, and an appropriate input switching arrangement is given in Figure 8 - 14.

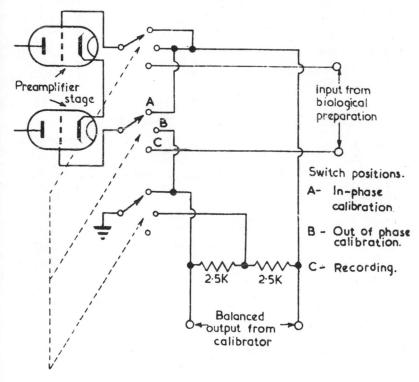

Fig. 8 - 14—Input switching circuit for the voltage calibrator. (By permission from *Electrophysiological technique*, by C. J. Dickinson, 1950, Electronic Engineering, London)

SOME SPECIALIZED PROBLEMS AND EQUIPMENTS

ELECTROENCEPHALOGRAPHY

Bipolar and monopolar leads.—Two common approaches are used in taking potentials from the scalp. One has each input lead to the amplifier come from an electrode which is located over an active cortical area. Such a system of leads is termed *bipolar* in the sense that both poles are over "live" or active areas. In the other instance, one electrode is placed over an active area, while the other is connected to an inactive area such as the lobe of the ear. Activity in this sense refers to the nearness to the source of cortical potential. Such a pickup is termed *monopolar*.

In general, bipolar leads give a continuous record of the changes in potential difference between the two electrodes. Interaction and interference effects exist between the activity of cells under each electrode. These lead to some specialized applications—for example, in the localization of cortical areas (i.e., finding tumors, activating centers, etc.) Monopolar leads, on the other hand, indicate chiefly the activity under the active electrode, or between the active electrode and the "neutral" electrode. Both monopolar and bipolar leads have advantages which make it necessary to consider them in relation to specific investigations (9).

Channels.—As typically employed, EEG equipment consists of several amplifiers—each with its own electrodes and recording mechanism. This makes possible the simultaneous recording of potentials picked up at different locations on the scalp. Each circuit with its pickup electrodes, amplifier, and recorder is called a channel. Commercial oscillographs usually contain four to eight channels with the recording pens mounted on a single polygraph (Fig. 8 - 15). In the use of multichannel equipment it is necessary to prevent interference or "cross talk" between channels.

Monopolar electrode placements.—Monopolar leads for a "typical" eight-channel recording would utilize the channels for

Fig. 8 - 15—A commercial electroencephalograph.
(Courtesy Grass Instrument Co., Quincy, Mass.)

the following areas: right frontal, left frontal, right temporal, left temporal, right parietal, left parietal, right occipital, and left occipital. One electrode would be placed on the lobe of each ear and connected to a common inactive lead to all channels (see Fig. 8 - 16). Frontal electrodes would be high on the forehead; parietal electrodes would be directly above right and left auditory canals and two or three centimeters from the midline. The occipital electrodes would be located about two centimeters above the occipital protuberance and two centimeters on either side of the midline. Temporal electrodes would be about halfway between the opening of the ear and the parietal electrode.

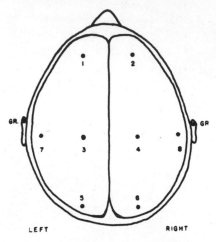

1 Left frontal
2 Right frontal
3 Left parietal
4 Right parietal
5 Left occipital
6 Right occipital
7 Left temporal
8 Right temporal

Fig. 8 - 16—Monopolar electrode placements. (From Ogilvie, *Manual of electroencephalography*, 1945, Addison-Wesley, Cambridge, Mass.)

Artifacts.—In all bioelectric measurements the problem of detecting errors in the record is an important one. Because of the high gain in EEG equipment the likelihood of picking up extraneous sources of electrical variation is great. Several sources of error have been mentioned earlier in connection with discussions of distortion and noise. Another major source arises from the confusion of brain potential changes with other physiological electrical changes which appear in the electrical field on the surface of the scalp. These include fluctuations due to changes in the resistance of the skin; action potentials of the muscles of the scalp, jaws, and neck, particularly those which accompany the blinking of the eyes; and even fluctuations due to the pulsing of arteries in the head. One can become familiar with the many sources of artifacts only through experience and careful study of the comparisons of error patterns with "true" patterns such as are given in standard references like Hill and Parr (19, pp. 53 - 54).

Shielding.—Still another source of difficulty which introduces artifacts in the record is pickup by the amplifier of stray electrostatic or electromagnetic fields. Much of this pickup is through the subject who may provide a high-resistance contact with the ground. To combat this source of disturbance, it is necessary either to ground the subject or carefully isolate him from ground. The most troublesome source of pickup is stray 60-cycle radiation.

Although many commercial electroencephalographs are constructed with filter systems and high-discrimination ratios to combat extraneous signal input, it is still common in research situations to have the subject in a shielded room or cage. One form of shield consists of chicken-wire screen or hardware cloth of $3/8$- or $1/2$-inch mesh which has been galvanized after weaving. Another consists of copper foil backed by heavy paper, or copper screen. The joints formed by separate strips of shielding are soldered about every two feet. All unnecessary sources of radiation are kept outside the screen, and such electrical apparatus as is required inside is independently shielded and carefully grounded, preferably to the same grounding terminal as the screen or shield.

There are also many sources of possible electrostatic interference on the surface of the subject's clothing, furniture, and electrostatic generating substances of all sorts, including the insulation on lead-in wires. For a further discussion of these problems see Gibbs and Gibbs (14) and Hill and Parr (19).

ELECTROCARDIOGRAPHS

Commercial instruments for the amplification and recording of potentials given off by muscles of the heart during con-

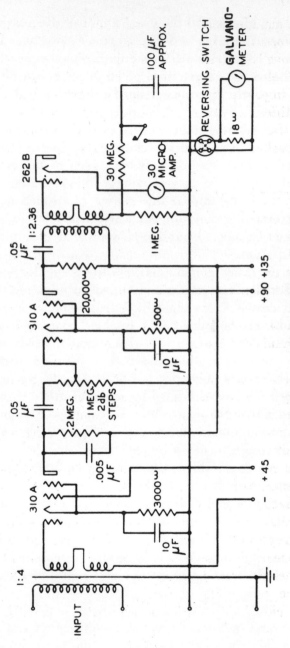

Fig. 8 · 17—A muscle potential integrator. (From Jacobsen [21] courtesy of the *Review of scientific instruments*)

traction are manufactured by a number of companies and are called *electrocardiographs*. Pickup is usually made from one or more "active" electrodes over the heart and various reference or "neutral" electrodes more distally located. The use of these instruments in psychology stems from the fact that they can be readily modified for general purpose muscle potential recording, or they can be used directly as indicators of heart action in such specialized studies as the conditioning of circulatory reactions.

MUSCLE POTENTIAL INTEGRATORS

In electromyography it is often desired that the amount of potential variation over a period of time be accumulated and recorded. The simplest device for accomplishing this leads the output of the amplifier into an auxiliary circuit which rectifies the action potentials and passes them on to the plates of a condenser as an accumulating charge (Fig. 8 - 17). The amount of charge on the condenser is thus a function of muscle activity and can be read by a ballistic galvanometer or a vacuum-tube voltmeter.

A similar device has the condenser charge accumulate with time until a given charge is reached. It then discharges through a gas-filled tube and activates an impulse counter, indicating the potential accumulated over a period of time by the number of counts.

A more recent device makes possible the cumulation of potential changes over a range of intervals of time (Fig. 8 - 18). The accumulating potentials across two condensers are passed on to the deflection plates of a cathode-ray oscillograph. The oscillograph pattern, which is photographed with a moving film, appears as a series of notches. The height of each notch indicates the total potential change in the interval. The length of the cumulating interval is controlled by a relay which, when closed, sets the condensers back to their original charge.

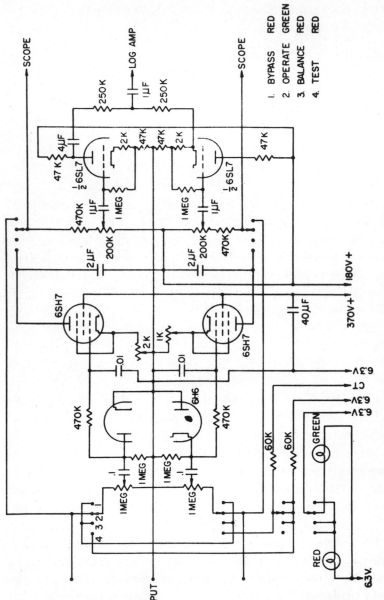

Fig. 8·18—A muscle potential integrator. (From Davis [17])

INPUT CIRCUITS IN ELECTRODERMAL MEASUREMENT

When resistance and impedance phenomena of the skin (rather than skin potentials) are observed, a specialized circuit is required to deliver an AC or DC voltage to the skin and reflect the resistance or impedance change as a voltage drop across the subject. Since many of these circuits vary markedly, a brief summary will be presented here.

Simple series circuit.—Perhaps the simplest arrangement for measuring skin resistance consists of a circuit with a battery, the subject, and a galvanometer in series. A change in the resistance of the subject is indicated by a deflection of the galvanometer. To make it possible to zeroize the galvanometer, a source of counter emf can be introduced. This circuit finds use for demonstration purposes only, for it is subject to a number of errors. The current through the subject is not constant, the deflections of the galvanometer are not directly proportional to the changes in the subject's resistance, and results obtainable are not comparable from one situation or individual to another. Most of these weaknesses can be overcome by putting a very large resistance in series and using the result as a series or bleeder circuit input to a high-gain amplifier (see Fig. 8 - 20). The sensitivity of this system is very low, and it has other inherent disadvantages.

Wheatstone bridges.—A bridge circuit is often used to measure skin resistance (11). It will be recalled that a Wheatstone bridge consists of four resistances occupying arms of a series parallel arrangement, with a current source spanning two of the arms and a galvanometer spanning the other two in such a way that no current flows through the galvanometer when the arms bear the correct ratio to one another. When, however, the bridge becomes unbalanced by an alteration in the resistance of one arm, current flows through the galvanometer. Such a bridge, making the subject the "unknown" resistance, is convenient to use, since it can be balanced after each trial or situation to allow for changes in the subject's base resistance.

Some models, however, give results which vary from situation to situation. They fail to allow for changes in sensitivity resulting from variations in the total resistance of the bridge and current through the subject.

The essential feature of the Wheatstone bridge for skin-resistance measurement (Fig. 8 - 19) is the maintenance of circuit constants (voltage across the bridge and current through

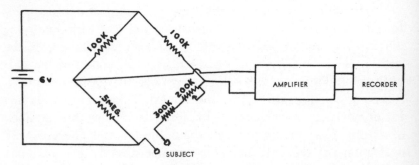

Fig. 8 - 19—A GSR amplifier with a Wheatstone bridge input

the bridge arms) at a single value at all times by placing the subject in series with a variable resistor in the "unknown" arm of the bridge. Variations in the base resistances of subjects may then be compensated for by changes in this series resistor without altering the current through the skin or the over-all resistance of the circuit. It is necessary that the total resistance of the subject's arm of the bridge be high to minimize changes in current caused by variations in the subject's resistance. This, in turn, reduces the sensitivity of the circuit, requiring either high amplification or the use of a very sensitive galvanometer.

Wynn-Williams bridge.—Another form of bridge circuit uses vacuum tubes in place of resistances in the subject's arm of the bridge and the arm occupied by the ratio resistance (Fig. 8 - 20). The left-hand tube is operating at a fixed bias, and the right-hand tube is operating at a bias which is influenced by changes in the resistance of the subject. When the bridge is balanced, no current flows in the meter branch. A change in the subject's resistance alters the bias on the right-hand tube, unbalancing the bridge in an amount proportional to the resistance change at the electrodes.

If the subject's circuit is employed as drawn, a large resistor is needed in series with the subject to minimize current changes resulting from changes in the subject's resistance. This

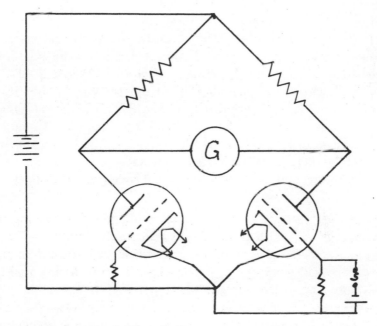

Fig. 8 - 20—A Wynn-Williams bridge GSR amplifier

in turn, reduces sensitivity. Since the input operates as a voltage divider (the total voltage drop across the battery is divided between the subject and the series resistor), the ratio of values is important. A large series resistor allows changes in base resistance from person to person and moment to moment to occur without materially affecting the total resistance of the circuit and the relative "dividing up" of the total voltage drop between the two resistances.

The apparatus as illustrated is essentially that employed by Haggard and Gerbrands (16). In slightly modified form it has been used extensively by physiologists in the measurement of muscle and nerve potentials. The circuit would function satisfactorily with numerous modifications. The left-hand tube could be replaced by a resistor with a resulting increase in sensitivity and decrease in stability, and an increase in gain could be obtained by substituting two tubes operating in parallel for the right-hand tube.

Alternating current series circuit.—A circuit designed to reduce electrode polarization difficulties by passing an alternating current through the subject is shown in Figure 8 - 21. A small AC current is passed through the subject and rectified by a meter-type dry-plate rectifier. The rectified current passes through a galvanometer in parallel with a source of counter emf. The initial resistance of the subject is obtained from the reading of the series resistance box necessary to zeroize the galvanometer, and the GSR is indicated by the meter deflection.

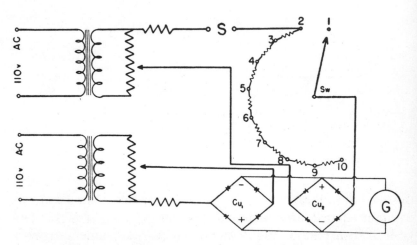

Fig. 8 - 21—An alternating current circuit for measuring the GSR. (From Grant [23] courtesy of the author and the *American journal of psychology*)

This circuit is basically a series circuit employing an alternating current to reduce polarization and a variable resistance for controlling current through the subject.

Potentiometric method.—A direct-current potentiometric technique has been used as shown in Figure 8 - 22. The poten-

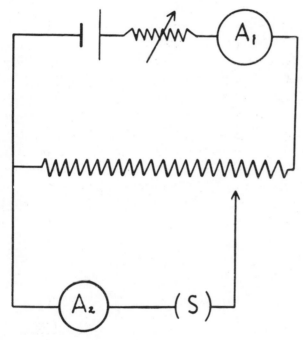

Fig. 8 - 22—A potentiometric GSR circuit. (From Lacey and Siegel [24] courtesy of the authors and the *American journal of psychology*)

tiometer is calibrated to indicate basic resistance levels with a constant current (40 microamperes) through the subject. The GSR is then read as the deflection of the microammeter from its initial position. The interpretation of changes in this circuit shares some of the complexities of the simple Wheatstone bridge.

Constant-current input.—Another input circuit designed
to supply a constant current through the subject and drive a DC
amplifier is shown in Figure 8 - 23. The pickup electrodes are
placed in the plate circuit of a vacuum tube. This puts the high
resistance of the tube in series with the subject and delivers the

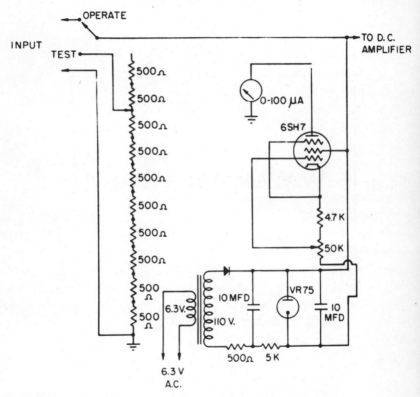

Fig. 8 - 23—A current stabilizing GSR input. (From Davis [17])

voltage drop across the subject to the amplifier. The level of
current through the subject is indicated on the meter and can
be varied by changing the grid bias on the tube. This particular
circuit is powered by a 6.3-volt source which is stepped up and
rectified. A series of resistances is provided which can be
switched in as a dummy subject for calibration purposes.

Carrier amplifiers.—Further possibilities exist in the use of conventional AC radio amplifiers as carrier amplifiers in recording the GSR. In fact, some of the commercial instruments operate on this principle. The procedure is feasible with either AC or DC current passing through the subject. If AC is used, the subject's impedance may be made to modulate the AC wave which is amplified and recorded by an AC voltmeter; or if DC is passed through the subject, the voltage drop thus developed can be used to modulate (as a volume control) the output of an audio oscillator.

Automatic range setting amplifiers.—One of the persistent problems in measuring the GSR is the inconvenience of manual adjustments of recording range which are necessitated by broad changes in a subject's base or activity level. A great deal of the experimenter's time is spent in maintaining a maximum recording sensitivity without losing part of the record due to the response overshooting the limit of the recording surface. Recently, investigators (17) and manufacturers (Yellow Springs Instrument Co., Yellow Springs, Ohio) have built into their apparatus devices for automatically adjusting the range. The procedure involves triggering of a servomotor or stepping switch when a given output signal value is exceeded (in either a positive or negative direction from a reference point). This action of the reset motor or stepping switch introduces new input circuit constants to the amplifier, thus automatically monitoring the output of the instrument.

Measurement units.—In considering GSR apparatus, it is necessary to raise the question of how to quantify the raw data. Because of the complexity of the phenomenon it is not possible to assign numbers to meter readings without asking certain measurement questions. It is ordinarily desirable to apply statistical methods to the results, to make individual and group comparisons, and to make comparisons within the scale of response values. All require knowledge of scale characteristics, such as: whether the units employed are equal throughout the scale and from situation to situation, whether physiological

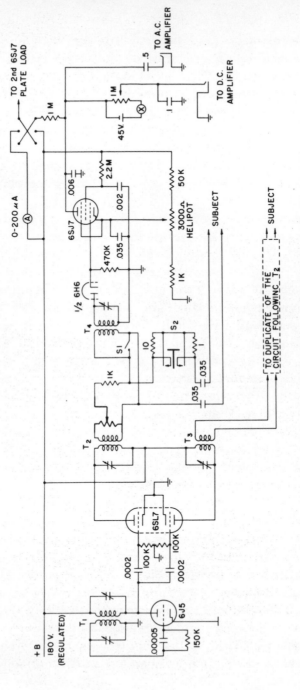

Fig. 8·24—An impedance plethysmograph. (From Davis [17])

effects are related to psychological, and whether the distribution of the measures for an unselect group is of a form appropriate for statistical tests.

These problems have been variously attacked by different investigators, and a rather extensive literature has resulted. Most of the references are listed in (13). Units suggested include ohms resistance, micromhos conductance, the logarithm of conductance, and various derived ratios. Each unit seems to be well fitted to certain situations or uses, but none is applicable to all. In light of existing evidence it appears necessary to conclude that the responsibility remains with the individual investigator to determine the appropriateness of the units he intends to use for a given situation.

IMPEDANCE PLETHYSMOGRAPH

The impedance of the body to a high-frequency current has been employed by some as an index of changes in tissue volume. The application is to infer from impedance changes the types of blood-volume changes throughout the body which have previously been picked up by pneumatic or hydraulic plethysmographs. Nyboer (28) applied electrodes to the fingers and secured simultaneous records of volume changes by the impedance method and mechanical pickup. Agreement was very high. The only psychological application of this potentially useful technique of which the writer is familiar is that by Davis (17) whose equipment is diagrammed in Figure 8 - 24.

ELECTRICAL STIMULATORS

Kinds.—There are four or five useful means for administering a controlled electric current (shock) to an organism. The simplest of these are illustrated in Figure 8 - 25. The oldest is the inductorium, consisting of two inductively coupled coils of wire with different numbers of turns and a vibrator for interrupting the current through the primary coil. As a stimulator for research purposes the inductorium has a number of disadvantages: the make and break shocks differ in intensity, the

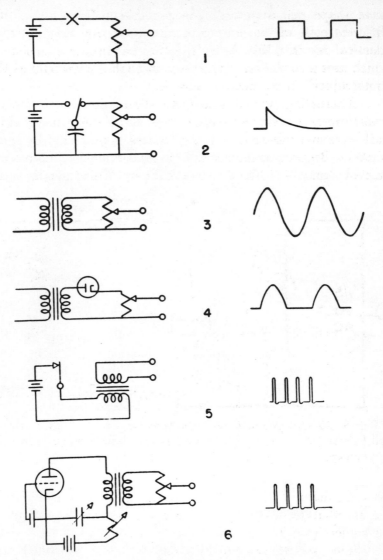

Fig. 8-25—Wave forms from different electric stimulators. (By permission from Erickson and Gilson [30] courtesy the author and publisher)

wave shape and amplitude are variable and irregular, and different coils of the same general construction may not give identical results (30). A modification has been recommended which uses a condenser discharging through a neon bulb as the "interrupter" in the primary circuit.

Alternating-current sine-wave stimulation from step-up transformers and sine-wave generators is sometimes used, while half-wave and full-wave rectified current is preferred by some workers. Because of their simplicity and economy, alternating current stimulators like that in Figure 8 - 26 and simple recti-

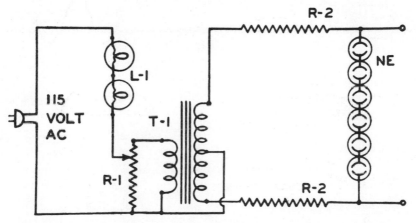

Fig. 8 - 26—An alternating-current shocking device. (From Mount and Lehner [26] courtesy of the authors and the *American journal of psychology*)

fiers like that in Figure 8 - 27 are common. In other instruments the essential feature is a condenser which discharges through the subject (see Fig. 8 - 25).

Some stimulators are modified vacuum-tube oscillators, usually in the form of a relaxation oscillator or a square-wave generator. The square-wave generator—so named because the output voltage pulse achieves its maximum instantaneously and remains at that level until returning instantaneously to its starting point (or opposite direction) value—is probably the best

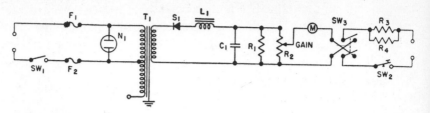

Fig. 8 - 27—Electric stimulator using rectified AC current. (From Humphrey [27] courtesy of the author and the *American journal of psychology*)

of these. The use of a rectangular pulse permits control of both the amplitude and duration of the impulse.

Precautions.—Whenever electrical stimulation systems are employed, careful consideration must be given to possible injurious effects to the organism; for surprisingly low currents through the body may produce death, especially when vital organs such as the heart lie in the course of the current. A tentative maximum current for safety devices, recommended at a symposium on the use of shock, is 12 milliamperes of 8 thousandths of a second duration (29). In a review of protective devices, fuses and circuit breakers (relays) were found to be too slow and unreliable for use with humans, and several electronic shock-control circuits were considered; only one of which was judged to function satisfactorily. Since that time improved fuses have become available, and new applications of shock (therapeutical) have given rise to improved electronic controls. The most important of these include devices (such as isolation transformers) for separating the subject from the source of current—or constant-voltage gas tubes or grid-controlled vacuum-tube circuits in parallel with the subject in such a way that, whenever a critical voltage is reached, the auxiliary circuit serves as a protective shunt to the subject (26).

REFERENCES

1. GLASSER, O. *Medical physics.* Chicago: Yearbook Publishers, Vol. 1, 1944, Vol. 2, 1950.

2. BRINK, F. Excitation and conduction in the neuron. Chap. 2 in STEVENS, S. S. (ed.) *Handbook of experimental psychology.* New York: John Wiley and Sons, 1951.

3. BRAZIER, M. A. B. *The electrical activity of the nervous system.* London: Pitman and Sons, 1951.

4. ERLANGER, J., and GASSER, H. S. *Electrical signs of nervous activity.* Philadelphia: University of Pennsylvania Press, 1937.

5. GELDARD, F. A. *The human senses.* New York: John Wiley and Sons, Inc., 1953.

6. BARTLEY, S. H. *Vision.* New York: D. Van Nostrand Co., Inc., 1941.

7. STEVENS, S. S., and DAVIS, H. *Hearing.* New York: John Wiley and Sons, Inc., 1938.

8. MORGAN, C. T., and STELLAR, E. *Physiological psychology.* New York: McGraw-Hill Book Co., Inc., 1950.

9. JASPER, H. H. Electrical signs of cortical activity, *Psychol. bull.,* 1937, 34, 411-481.

10. LOOMIS, A. L., HARVEY, E. N., and HOBART, C. G. Electrical potentials of the human brain, *J. exp. psychol.,* 1936, 19, 249-279.

11. WOODWORTH, R. S. *Experimental psychology.* New York: Henry Holt and Co., 1938. (Chap. 13.)

12. LANDIS, C. Electrical phenomena of the skin, *Psychol. bull.,* 1932, 29, 693-752.

13. GRINGS, W. W. Methodological considerations underlying electrodermal measurement, *J. psychol.,* 1953, 35, 271-282.

14. GIBBS, F. A., and GIBBS, E. L. *Atlas of electroencephalography.* Boston: Addison Wesley Press, 1950.

15. DICKINSON, C. J. *Electrophysiological technique.* London: Electronic Engineering, 1950.

16. HAGGARD, E. A., and GERBRANDS, R. An apparatus for the measurement of continuous changes in palmar skin resistance, *J. exp. psychol.,* 1947, 37, 92-98.

17. DAVIS, R. C. Personal communication; and a report entitled *A report of research on detection of deception,* performed by Indiana University under contract with the Office of Naval Research, Sept. 1952, D. C. Ellson, Project director.

18. TRUEBLOOD, H., and GRINGS, W. W. A DC amplifier for GSR and low-frequency potential measurement, *J. psychol.,* 1950, 30, 401-403.

19. HILL, D., and PARR, G. *Electroencephalography.* New York: Macmillan Co., 1950. Also OGILVIE, R. S. *Handbook of electroencephalography.* Cambridge, Mass.: Addison Wesley Press, 1949.

20. COHN, R. *Clinical electroencephalography.* New York: McGraw-Hill Book Co., Inc., 1949.

21. JACOBSON, E. An integrating voltmeter for the study of nerve and muscle potentials, *Rev. sci. instr.* 1940, 11, 415-418.

22. DAVIS, R. C. An integrator and accessory apparatus for recording action potentials, *Amer. j. psychol.*, 1948, 61, 100-103.

23. GRANT, D. A. A convenient alternating current circuit for measuring GSRs, *Amer. j. psychol.*, 1946, 59, 149-151.

24. LACEY, O. L., and SIEGEL, P. S. An improved potentiometric circuit for measuring the galvanic skin response, *Amer. j. psychol.*, 1948, 61, 272-274.

25. DAVIS, R. C., and PORTER, J. M. A measuring device for the galvanic skin reflex, *J. gen. psychol.*, 1931, 5, 115-120.

26. MOUNT, G. E., and LEHNER, G. F. J. The use of certain electronic tubes in the psychological laboratory, *Amer. j. psychol.*, 1948, 61, 247-259.

27. HUMPHREY, C. E. A simplified stimulus generator, *Amer. j. psychol.*, 1953, 66, 122-123.

28. NYBOER, J. Plethysmograph: impedance. In GLASSER, O. *Medical physics.* Chicago: Yearbook Publishing Co., Vol. 2., 1950. Also NYBOER, J., BAGNO, S., and NIMS, L. F. The impedance plethysmograph: an electrical volume recorder. National Research Council Committee on Aviation Medicine. *Rep. No. 149,* 1943.

29. FORBES, T. W., MUENZINGER, K. F., and WENDT, G. R. Report of round tables on use of electric shock, *Psychol. bull.*, 1935, 32, 197-202. MAX, L. W. Protective devices and precautions against lethal shock. *Psychol. bull.*, 1935, 32, 203-211.

30. ERICKSON, T. C., and GILSON, W. E. Electrical stimulation in the study of cortical function, pp. 348-352 in GLASSER, O. *Medical physics.* Chicago: Yearbook publishers, Vol. 1, 1944.

Index

275